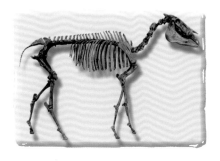

A skeleton frozen in time ...

...*preserved in a sage plateau of toothed and twisted formations*...

...uncovered in a Magic Valley dammed for irrigation ...

...reveals a timeless chaos—a nature more complex than Darwin once imagined, a process both fitful and catastrophic that shaped the progress of civilization as desert landscapes evolved.

Cover

Hipparion primigenium from Höwenegg Quarry, Germany. Now extinct, this European three-toed horse is a descendant of the North American "dawn-horse" that migrated to Eurasia ten million years ago, thus anticipating the later migration of the modern horse, one-toed *Equus,* by 7.5 million years.

Photos

Shoshone Falls on the Snake River. Previous pages: Little City of Rocks near Gooding; Milner Dam tunnel construction, Twin Falls County, 1905.

Moragootch, a Snake River Shoshone, 1884

secrets

of the **magic**

VALLEY AND

hagerman's

REMARKABLE

horse

Black Canyon Communications, LLC
Published in cooperation with
Hagerman Fossil Council, Inc. and
Boise State University History Department

Todd Shallat
editor

Kathryn Baxter
managing editor

Adele Thomsen
graphics designer

James Frost
staff photographer

Kathryn Baxter
James Frost
Ronald L. James
H. Gregory McDonald
Kelly A. Murphey
Todd Shallat
Bob Willhite
authors

Peter Bowler
Mathew Henbest
Paul Link
Ambrose Richardson
Spencer Woods
contributors

Neil King
Superintendent, Hagerman
Fossil Beds National Monument

Black Canyon Communications, LLC
offers entertaining and informative
books about the human encounter
with nature in the American West.

http://www.blackcanyon
communications.com

Owyhee Plaza Hotel, Suite 331
P. O. Box 9501
Boise, ID 83707

208-345-9900

Balloon-framed barn, Twin Falls County

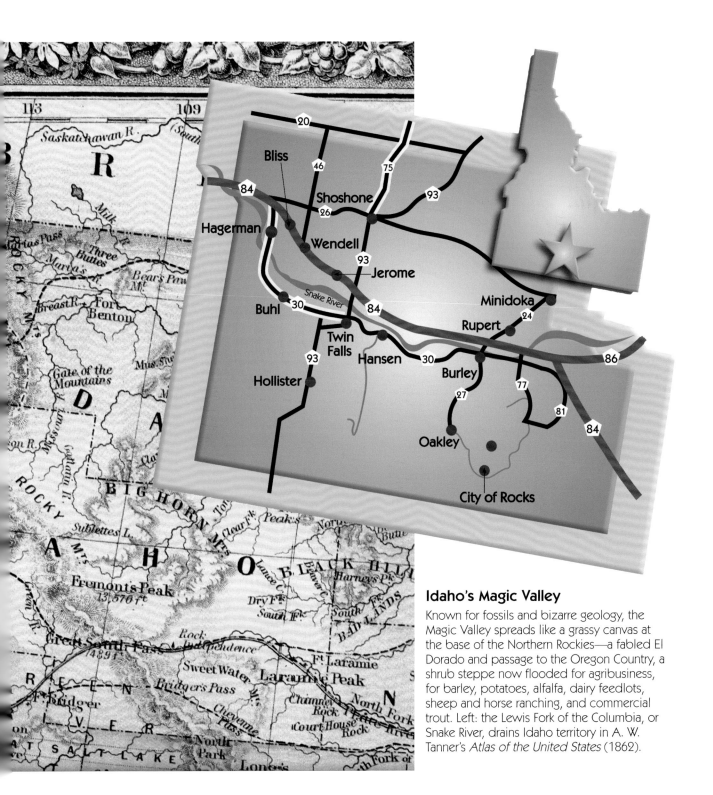

Idaho's Magic Valley

Known for fossils and bizarre geology, the Magic Valley spreads like a grassy canvas at the base of the Northern Rockies—a fabled El Dorado and passage to the Oregon Country, a shrub steppe now flooded for agribusiness, for barley, potatoes, alfalfa, dairy feedlots, sheep and horse ranching, and commercial trout. Left: the Lewis Fork of the Columbia, or Snake River, drains Idaho territory in A. W. Tanner's *Atlas of the United States* (1862).

Secrets of the Magic Valley began with the realization that history, like evolutionary science, is narrative simplification. Just as Charles Darwin presented his data as progress through competition, the history of America's West is a pageant traditionally skewed as a sequence of heroic events. Our book about horse and Man in Idaho's magical desert suggests alternative views. Collectively written, the project evolved from seven research essays anthologized as *A Natural History of the Hagerman National Monument* (2002), edited by Kathryn Baxter and available from Black Canyon Communications.

We gratefully acknowledge vital assistance from Julie Gale, Guen Johnson, Carol Mitchell, Gwenetta Bates, Merle Wells, Bob Fullilove, Gail Seaman, Bill Roe, Mark Plew, Bob Evancho, Linda Parkinson, Kathy Hodges, Marilyn Buckendorf, Aaron Campbell, Jennifer Flint, Barton Barbour, Max Pavesic, Robert McCarl, James Woods, Bill West, Errol Jones, Peter Buhler, Robert Sims, Carol MacGregor, Mary Carter, Alan Virta, Ralph Peters, Karen Quinton, Jody Hawley Ochoa, Linda Morton-Keithly, Carolyn Bowler, Vince Alberdi, Charles Scheer, Brian Warthen, John Kelly, Larry Burke, Ron Schuler, Gary Keith, Ken Swanson, Kathleen Mortensen, Tina Vader, Judi Hart, Neal Farmer, Phil Gensler, Dick Cook, Grove Koger, Adrian Taylor, and the Hagerman Fossil Council.

Thousand Springs near Hagerman

Snake River at Salmon Falls

Contents

Paving mixer, Twin Falls, 1910

◆ **Kathryn Baxter, M.A.**
History, Boise State University
Peter Bowler, Ph.D.
Evolutionary Biology, University of California, Irvine
Paul Link, Ph.D.
Geology, Idaho State University
Spencer Woods, Ph.D.
Geosciences, Boise State University

Magic Mirror

CHAPTER ONE

Many years ago, when the great buffalo herds still grazed the plains, two lovers tryst-ed above a mighty waterfall the Shoshone called Pah-chu-laka—hurling waters leaping. Every night the strong warrior met his slender maiden on a smooth rock that overlooked the foaming green cascade. One day he went away to lift the scalps of white men. She never doubted his return, but many moons grew full and died away. Still, she waited faithfully each night on the water's brink. Then one night, a warrior stepped from the deep shadows and whispered in her ear. After he disappeared, she stood a long time looking down into the cauldron that threw sparkling mist at the stars. Her arms lifted slowly, then her proud head. She poised on tiptoe for a moment and dived into the wild roar, shattering the mirror of water. "Since that hour," spoke Quish-in-demi, "the river has never been the same."

Idaho's Magic Valley reflects a storied place. Its legends and myths serve to explain what environmental historian Mark Fiege calls "our deeply entangled and problematic rela-

tionship to the natural world." A landscape like the Magic Valley's remarkable lava, lost rivers, hidden canyons, and epic falls "is not just a place," he says. "It is a story." A wilderness transformed by water, it tells how life persisted and evolved against incredible odds. When people impacted the valley, they created new environments. Shoshone legend saw the Snake River changed when a maiden gave her life to its awesome power. Engineer D. W. Ross, in 1894, saw the Snake River changed when its terrible force was "harnessed [and] made to do the work of half a million horses." Humans alter nature, but nature bites back in a continuous process that results in a mythic landscape both human and natural with surprising secrets and unexpected twists.

The Magic Valley lies at the heart of the Snake River Plain, in a southern Idaho crescent that sweeps east to west, border to border, dipping south from Rupert to Twin Falls. Designated magic by promoters in the early 1900s, the valley's regional identity extends west from Caldron Linn to Glenns Ferry, north from Jackpot to Sun Valley. Its population of over 150,000 covers eight counties—Blaine, Cassia, Minidoka, Jerome, Lincoln, Twin Falls, Gooding, and Camas. Its culture resides in small towns like Eden, Hansen, Kimberly, Jerome, Filer, Buhl, Wendell, Hagerman, Bliss, and Gooding. Water has always worked its magic here. Prehistoric seabeds left coral and

Stretching from Burley to Bliss, from the Sawtooths to Jackpot, the valley takes its name from a staircase of water projects that reclaimed as if by magic the fertile crescent of the Snake River Plain. Above: white water at Milner. Right: Richfield Canal. Previous: lightning strikes Snake River grasslands.

ammonites on later desert steppes. Floods uncovered fossils radioactive from water-leached uranium. Irrigation drawn from an underground aquifer system like Hawaii's bloomed a sage-brush plateau that lies on lava identical to the moon's. Today the sound of sprinklers vies with the rush of canyon rapids.

"Topographically," wrote historian Vardis Fisher, "Idaho is one of the strangest States in the Union ... the last frontier, delivered to rock and desolation." His 1937 view echoed the voices of westward travelers whose eastern experience of land gave them little vision or vocabulary to interpret the plain's geography. They had to invent new ways to see and describe. As they did their sense of the place evolved, and so did the stories surrounding it. A written-off wilderness was now recognized as a singular place. Explorer Clarence King's desert waste became Washington Irving's picturesque

Melon boulders. Right: Archie B. Teater 's *Cattle Grazing in Hills* frames a flood-swept Hagerman landscape.

landscape. Natural wonders became natural resources. Wilderness became monuments, and monuments became part of what Wallace Stegner called "the geography of hope."

That hope stemmed from the western version of the ancient garden myth. In 1893, Frederick Jackson Turner made manifest destiny a frontier imperative and recast the garden myth to fit the American wilderness. Turner's frontier thesis pictured humanity conquering western wildness and claiming it for productive use. In turn, the process of making the desert bloom produced the uniquely American traits born on the frontier: "that dominant individualism, working for good and for evil, and withal that buoyancy and exuberance which comes with freedom." Eden was found, mankind redeemed, and American identity forged in the crucible.

Each successive wave of civilization Turner described passed across the Magic Valley, and each brought its own view of the place. Indians thought Shoshone Falls a powerful totem, and fur trappers called it a navigational block. Oregon Trail emigrants stood speechless at its sublime chaos, and miners knew it as the liquid gold that brought placer gold from upriver. Homesteaders harnessed it for hydraulic power and pro-

moted it as a tourist attraction. Scientists used it as a window into the earth. But the Magic Valley existed long before humanity came to imprint it—a dynamic landscape with its own identity distinct from those who later claimed it.

Rivers of Stone

The Magic Valley's origins lie deep in antiquity and basalt. Fifteen million years ago, the North American continental plate drifted over a hot spot, a place where semimolten magma erupts from the earth's crust and flows out as lava. This black basalt layers the Snake River Plain hundreds of feet deep and covers a trail of ancient volcanoes that slowly moved east to Yellowstone as the continent moved west. The hot spot responsible for the Magic Valley's fractured cliffs and ragged rock piles originated where Idaho meets Oregon and Nevada. The volcanoes that emerged over it were violent, exploding clouds of gas and rhyolite ash miles into the air. Heavy basalt magma followed in flows over millions of years. The Snake River Canyon today is banded in rhyolite red and basalt black.

As the crust moved over the hot spot, scorching magma bulged it into a 900-miles-wide rift that collapsed into a great basin. Lake Idaho filled this basin 10 million years ago

and covered southern Idaho. The mammoth lake rose and fell over millennia as the climate changed; at its highest it reached 3,800 feet above sea level. Basalt continued to ooze beneath the water, forming glassy pillow lava shelves, thick cones, and twisted pillars—the unique geologic markers Fisher called "so varied and sometimes so appalling." A tiny tributary of the Salmon River eventually cut its way through to Lake Idaho a million years ago. The water flooded north up the tributary in a huge drainage that ultimately created Hells Canyon and left behind the Snake River. All the streams that fed the lake were left high above its bed to erode out the canyons that score the plain today.

Right: the Ice Age returned to the Snake at Perrine Coulee in this 1930s photograph.

During the life of Lake Idaho, sediments from gravel, sand, silt, and volcanic ash settled on the lakebed in the Glenns Ferry formation, a deposit covering the Snake River Plain up to 1,700 feet thick. About the time the lake drained, almost half the species alive then went extinct, their fossils preserved in the sediment. Buried in the porous basalt beneath the formation flows an underground water network called the Snake River Aquifer. Snowmelt and rainfall feed the aquifer, and the aquifer feeds the Snake, sometimes spectacularly. Thousand Springs near Hagerman cascades white against black canyon walls in some of the biggest springs in the United States.

The Glenns Ferry formation provided a spillway for another ancient lake. The McKinney Butte volcano nine miles northeast of Bliss poured basalt across the plain and into the Snake River Canyon, creating a natural lava dam southwest of Bliss that backed water upriver past Thousand Springs. Lake McKinney lay 600 feet deep at the dam. When clay deposits sealed

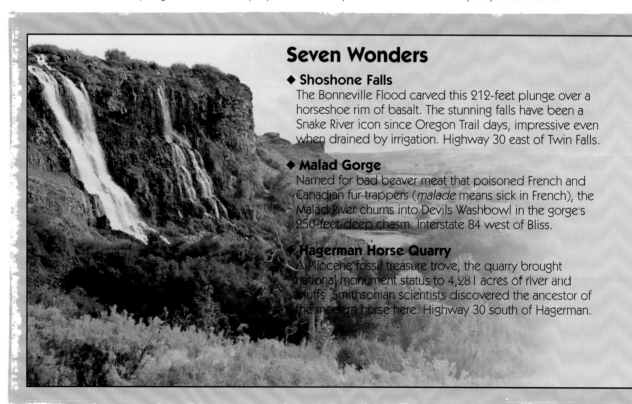

Seven Wonders

◆ Shoshone Falls
The Bonneville Flood carved this 212-feet plunge over a horseshoe rim of basalt. The stunning falls have been a Snake River icon since Oregon Trail days, impressive even when drained by irrigation. Highway 30 east of Twin Falls.

◆ Malad Gorge
Named for bad beaver meat that poisoned French and Canadian fur trappers (*malade* means sick in French), the Malad River churns into Devils Washbowl in the gorge's 250-feet-deep chasm. Interstate 84 west of Bliss.

◆ Hagerman Horse Quarry
A Pliocene fossil treasure trove, the quarry brought national monument status to 4,281 acres of river and bluffs. Smithsonian scientists discovered the ancestor of the modern horse here. Highway 30 south of Hagerman.

the porous lava, water spilled across the formation's soft sediments and eroded a new canyon south of the old one. The pillow basalts that flowed into the lake behind the dam lie exposed in canyon outcrops today.

The last great Ice Age accounted for the last great flood on the plain. Lake Bonneville slowly rose to fill the Great Salt Lake basin. Cooler temperatures reduced its evaporation, and the precipitation that fed mountain glaciers increased its volume until it poured over the natural dam at Red Rock Pass near Pocatello about 14,500 years ago. Its torrent cut the little canyon 350 feet deeper in an output greater than the Amazon's annual flow. In the Magic Valley, the flood filled the river canyon, scouring walls and cutting deeper. It left behind a series of steep rapids in the gorge and falls like the stunning Shoshone near Twin Falls, taller than Niagara at 212 feet high. The big "melon gravel" boulders around Hagerman stand as witness to the deluge that covered the valley here eighty-five feet deep with sediment.

◆ **Box Canyon**
This black basalt cut, invisible except at its rim, deeply slices cultivated farmland. The hidden spring at the canyon's base pools incredibly blue and streams out to the Snake River. Highway 30 southeast of Hagerman.

◆ **Gooding City of Rocks and Little City of Rocks**
Richly colored shale and sandstone rise up in pillars, spires, and pyramids that overlook two deep canyons. Sculpted by water, wind, and sand, the rocks present a four-mile panorama. Highway 46 north of Gooding.

◆ **Niagara Springs**
One of the least developed of the spectacular Thousand Springs, this Natural National Landmark pours out up to 300 cubic feet of water per second, water filtered pure through lava and perfect for trout. Interstate 84 south of Wendell.

◆ **Shoshone Ice Caves**
A glacier lives beneath the desert in lava flows left behind by the hot spot that now bubbles sulfur pools in Yellowstone. Ice eight to thirty feet deep and ice crystals on the walls chill the long cavern. Highway 75 north of Shoshone.

Thousand Springs

The Ice Age also spawned more subtle events than catastrophic floods. For millennia the Snake River Plain's climate had been subtropical, warm and humid. After the formation of the Snake, volcanism subsided and it grew more arid. The Ice Age ushered in a million and a half years of cooler, wetter conditions that spread freshwater lakes and stream-fed marshes across the plain. After the Bonneville Flood, the climate warmed again. Increased evaporation dried up lakes, and decreased precipitation shrunk snowpacks. Wind drove the fine silt sediments called loess from western lakebeds in giant clouds. Loess filled every crevice, blanketed the plain, and drifted into towering dunes like the ones at Bruneau. Today it covers a desert steppe that grows potatoes, grain, and beans when it is irrigated, sagebrush when it is not.

Life & Limb

Life did not wait for the landscape to settle. From microscopic to mammoth, it took hold on the plain in successive waves. Swamps and marshes supported tree palms, rhinos, and four-toed horses fifty million years ago. Thirty million years later, horses had lost a toe and grazed with camels in redwood, oak, maple, and willow forests that also hid saber-toothed cats. When the Cascade Mountains to the west uplifted five million years ago, they blocked the rain and created an arid grassland bordered with pine where mastodons, giant sloths, and bears joined the first ancestors of modern horses on the range. In Ice Age times, aboriginal humans saw musk ox, beaver, and bison added to the plain's populations.

Ancient Lake Idaho's oxygen-rich shallows contained some ninety species of mollusks. Most of them died when the lake dried. Their small bodies sank into the Glenns Ferry sediments to make fossils that help track the history of the Snake River drainage and early life in the Magic Valley. Amazingly, one member survived. The Bliss Rapids snail is the only living mollusk native to a river west of the Continental Divide, and the only member of its North American family to reproduce asexually. About the diameter of the date stamped on a penny, it lives in fast-water habitats below Lower Salmon Falls Dam and Bliss Dam, and in Thousand Springs and the spring at Box Canyon. The Bliss Rapids snail has persisted for more than three million years in spite of the volcanism and climate swings that continually rocked its habitat. Today, pollution and the artificial adjustment of river levels make it an endangered species candidate.

The white sturgeon in the Snake River belong to a primitive family far more ancient than the snails. When teleosts began evolving the bony skeletons that distinguish modern fishes about 200 million years ago, the sturgeon kept its softer cartilage skeleton. Its barbed hide and unique spawning habits helped it adapt to grow as long as twelve feet and live as long as a century. Unlike salmon, sturgeon survive after they spawn, repeating the long migration upriver many times. The Hagerman reach of the Snake provided good habitat, and fishermen capitalized on the abundant fish at the turn of the twentieth century. They pickled, dried, or smoked its flesh and collected its eggs for the caviar market, though area Indians seemed to prefer the more easily caught salmon. Dams dramatically decreased the Magic Valley sturgeon population. Today, Snake River aquaculture offers the best hope for reestablishing it.

Balanced Rock near Castleford. Below: trophy grizzly from an Idaho postcard, about 1920. Left: car-sized Idaho white sturgeon.

Water Makes Magic

"Nature is dramatic in Idaho," wrote Harold Rhodenbaugh for *The Idaho Statesman* in 1929. "All of nature is significant, nothing is irrelevant or useless." Most significant of all for the arid West was water. Environmental historian Donald Worster distinguished western hydraulics as something "more than an advanced version of modern agribusiness." This region's irrigators did not buy water from time to time for mere production enhancement; they needed it to survive. "The western farmer ... lives or dies by the level of water in his ditches." Pioneers streamed into the wilderness with a mandate to use it. Not until the late nineteenth century did wilderness preservation conflict with the critical necessities of the garden myth. Dams brought the debate to the Snake River. "Man, the magician, has entered this once desolate region," a citizen wrote in the first decade of the new century, "and, with a touch of his wand of gold, has bestowed water on millions of acres of desert land." In 1970, the long national fray divided the Magic Valley over what to do about Thousand Springs.

"No one owns water in Idaho," said Keith Higginson, director of the Idaho Department of Water Administration. "You can, however, own a right to divert and use water for some beneficial purpose." Norman Standal thought his fish hatchery was beneficial, both commercially and environmentally. But in the summer of 1970, his Hagerman aquaculture operation faced fire from people concerned the new industry would use up a landmark. Standal said he laid out his hatchery to make the falls at Thousand Springs accessible to the public, and his preservation efforts "actually increased Horsetail Falls from 15 to 60 feet in height by simply digging the rock away." He cited runoff from cow pastures as a greater pollutant than fish hatcheries, which had

Sprinkler irrigation in Hagerman Valley. Below: Magic Valley power station pump house, about 1915.

A Magic Valley

Idaho's Magic Valley rose like a desert phoenix on the bombast of promotional writing. Milner Dam above Twin Falls was "the certain prophecy of a prosperous civilization," said a booster in 1907. Left: Gooding's water nymph from a Union Pacific brochure, about 1910. Below: Idaho corn harvest.

←—To Boise

For genial showers you need not wait
You only have to hoist the gate,
And let the waters overflow,
Our valleys rich in Idaho.

A Song of Idaho, 1905

Magic Valley Profiled:

Area:	10,115 sq. miles
Population 2000:	162,397
Croplands:	1,463,245 acres
Pasture & Range:	1,278,295 acres

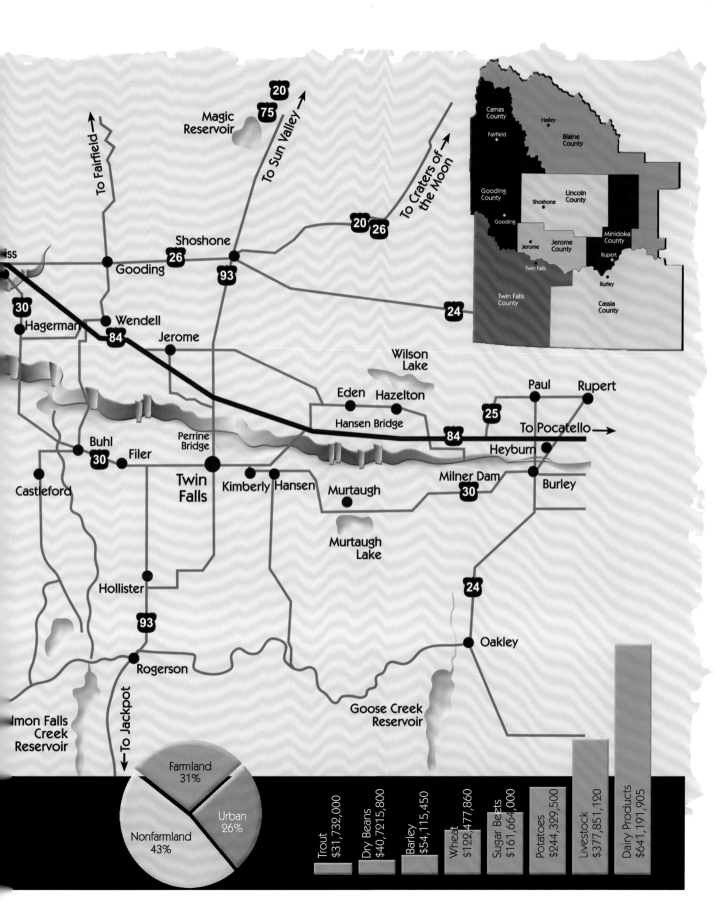

To Fairfield →

Magic
Reservoir

20
75
To Sun Valley →

To Craters of
the Moon →

iss

Gooding
Shoshone
26
93
20
26

24

30
Hagerman
Wendell
Jerome
84

Wilson
Lake

Eden
Hazelton
Paul
Rupert

Hansen Bridge
25
84
To Pocatello →

Buhl
Perrine
Bridge
Heyburn

30
Filer
Twin
Falls
Kimberly
Hansen
Murtaugh
Milner Dam
Burley

Castleford
30

Murtaugh
Lake

Hollister

24

93

Oakley

Rogerson

To Jackpot →

Goose Creek
Reservoir

lmon Falls
Creek
Reservoir

Camas County
Hailey
Fairfield
Blaine County
Gooding County
Shoshone
Lincoln County
Gooding
Minidoka County
Jerome
Jerome County
Rupert
Twin Falls
Burley
Twin Falls County
Cassia County

Farmland
31%

Urban
26%

Nonfarmland
43%

Trout $31,732,000	Dry Beans $40,7215,800	Barley $54,115,450	Wheat $122,477,860	Sugar Beets $161,664,000	Potatoes $244,329,500	Livestock $377,851,120	Dairy Products $641,191,905

switched from horsemeat to scientifically prepared food. Standal claimed when his waters were tested, "they [came] out clear as a swimming pool."

The Idaho Environmental Council claimed otherwise. According to their attorney, Bruce

Bowler, aquaculture "requires not only the water, and pollution of it, but also clearing and bulldozing the land ... the kind of things that scar the landscape." The council also feared Idaho Power's impact. Once like Niagara, Thousand Springs was now a disappointment, Bowler said, "because it's not a thousand ... it's only about four." Idaho Power did run the flow from many of the springs through flumes to electrical generation turbines. Moreover, said Hagerman resident Aldrich Bowler, "They were very secretive about how and who they were letting land out to." Bowler believed Idaho Power released land for aquaculture to help protect its own water rights in the area. Idaho Power's vice president of engineering and operations, Glenn J. Hall, countered with the company's history of releasing land for recreational purposes to such organizations as the State Parks Department, the Boy Scouts, and the State

Fish and Game Department. As for water use, Hall said, "The plant does not consume the water it utilizes for electric power generation. It does not heat nor contaminate water. It does not interfere with fishing. It does not decrease the river flow."

Thirty years later, some of the Thousand Springs still pour from basalt cliffs, and aquaculture thrives in the Magic Valley. It has even taken an exotic turn. The aquifer-filtered water—hard, alkaline, and oxygenated—is not only perfect for trout, sturgeon, tilapia, and catfish; it works for alligators and tropical fish, too. Alligators answered Buhl fish farmer Leo Ray's dead fish disposal problem. They also gave him a new market for meat and finished hide products like purses, belts, and

boots. Ray mixes water from the hot geothermal springs with cold surface water for the warm environment the alligators need. The University of Idaho's Hagerman Fish Culture Experiment

Station does the same for its tropical fish. Researcher Ron Hardy sees multimillion-dollar potential in the tanks of ornamental zebra fish, neon tetras, discus fish, and angel fish. Ornamentals sell for almost three times the price of caviar and top trout by more than $20 a pound, a lucrative possibility for the valley's hundred hatcheries.

Preservation and use still define the evolving environmental landscape here. "To leak or not to leak" is the question today for Magic Valley water management, according to groundwater geologist Neal Farmer. The Snake River splits the region in more ways than one. On the east side of the canyon in Hagerman Valley, irrigators intentionally leak water from canals and holding ponds to replenish the aquifer they pump from. Leaking also helps offset irrigation's draw on surface water that can decrease springs like the one in Box Canyon. On the west side of the canyon, irrigators line ponds and canals to reduce seepage and conserve water. This

practice created "perched" aquifers by raising water levels unnaturally high above the regional Snake River Aquifer. Leaking produces cattails and other greenery incongruent to the arid canyon slopes. Not leaking produces landslides.

Farmer calls Hagerman Valley "the landslide capital of Idaho." It lies at the boundary of a major geologic contact running east to west through the Snake River Plain. Slope failures like the huge block failures in Malad Gorge are an ancient phe-

Bluffs near Hagerman Fossil Beds slide toward the Snake. Left: Geologist Neal Farmer overlooks the national monument. Below left: a relief map shows the flat volcanic depression of the eastern Snake River Plain. Previous: Hagerman trout farm; stacking hay near Buhl.

nomenon, but eight slides in the area since 1979 seem more than natural. "Mix in water," Farmer says, "and they start popping off." Idaho Power reservoirs raised canyon water levels as much as 40 feet, saturating sediments and undercutting slopes. Irrigation added to the instability. But the story is not simple. When agriculture first developed on the plain at the turn of the century, reclamation projects diverted water from the river and delivered it to the desert steppes. A large part of that water seeped into the underlying basalt, flowing through the porous lava and feeding back into the area's natural springs. Flood irrigation actually increased the flow of Thousand Springs until the 1950s, when sprinkler technologies turned the trend around. Water harnessed by humans might trigger land-slides, but it has also increased subterranean groundwater storage by millions of acre feet.

Pioneers came west to find Eden and fell from grace again. The garden myth hinged on a contra-diction: people were to conquer the same untouched nature they needed to redeem themselves. No sooner had they pushed back the wilderness than they clamored to restore it, and the new age of environmental-ism saw almost any human intervention as exploitive. While the West did experience what Worster called "a ruthless assault on nature," the landscape has adapted and per-sisted just as the peo-ple on it have, not in Turner's straight-line progression but in cycles and seasons. "As Idaho's irrigated landscape demon-strates," Fiege wrote, "our activities are not always opposed to nature and do not necessarily dominate or wreck it." Mankind's capacity to con-trol the environment is matched by nature's capacity to stamp mankind, a story of symbiosis. Maybe author Norman MacLean offers a landscape perspective as good as any: what we see plus what we know equals a beauty different than the sum of its parts.

Idaho irrigator. Right: the Silent City of Rocks above Almo in Cassia County seemed "naked and piled high with the most fantastic shapes," wrote an emigrant '49er from Hudspeth's Cutoff, a dangerous trail to California.

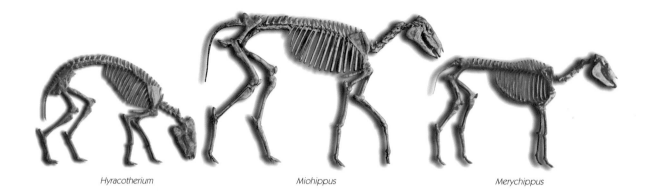

Hyracotherium   Miohippus   Merychippus

Hyracotherium 55–45 million years ago. The oldest known horse was a four-toed browser that foraged on nonfibrous foods. Its molars showed the beginning of horse-like ridges better suited for grazing.

Miohippus 33–29 mya. This small, two-toed browser was responsible for a burst of diverse side branches in the horse family. Its descendants were numerous and distinct.

Merychippus 17–11 mya. The first grazing horse had strong, crested teeth that enabled it to eat abrasive grasses. Even with primitive three-toed feet, its long legs equipped it for quick escapes and long-distance migrations.

Equus 5 mya. The single survivor of the formerly diverse horse genus, its living species include horses, asses, and zebras. Domestication of *Equus* 3,000 years ago dramatically impacted the world's civilizations by facilitating agriculture, migration, and warfare.

Equus

◆ **H. Gregory McDonald, Ph.D.**
  Director of Science and Paleontology
University of Colorado Museum

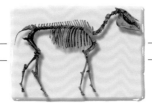

Equus Evolves

CHAPTER TWO

The mystique of the horse seems universal. It is a survivor, a relic of the past, a reminder of a primeval and very different Earth. Today there are eight species of horses, including zebras, donkeys, asses, burros, onagers, kulans, kiangs, and domestic horses, as well as the recently extinct quagga. All eight living species belong to the genus *Equus*, the Latin word for horse and the source for the term *equestrian*. However, the horses preserved in the fossil record represent as many as

six to eight genera, with each genus having numerous species. Although scientists once upheld the horse as a model of linear sequence, that model no longer applies.

Despite the horse's ancient success, by 3.7 million years ago the number of genera fell to three in North America. Members included a small form known as *Nannippus*, a larger rel-

ative called *Cormohipparion*, and *Equus*. The first two genera represent lineages with a long history starting sixteen million years ago. Both ultimately became extinct, leaving no descendants. In contrast, *Equus*, a relative latecomer geologically speaking, first appeared only 3.7 million years ago. The genus quickly adapted and diversified, eventually dispersing from North America into Asia, Europe, and Africa where its descendants still survive.

What was it about *Equus* that made its survival possible when all other types of horses became extinct? Paleontologists look for answers in the anatomy and ecology of Hagerman's *Equus simplicidens*. By examining the fossilized remains of the earliest known species of *Equus*, science can better explain why the horse lineage survived.

A Running Machine

We refer to the earliest known species of *Equus* as the "Hagerman Horse" in reference to the large sample from the Smithsonian Horse Quarry, located within Hagerman Fossil Beds National Monument and managed by the National Park Service. However, the scientific history of this species actually goes back to the close of the nineteenth century. In 1892, paleontologist Edward Drinker Cope first described *Equus simplicidens*. Cope found the original specimen, a single tooth, near Mount Blanco, Crosby County, Texas. Later discoveries of horses from similar age deposits elsewhere in the United States resulted in the description of other species of *Equus*.

Sometimes these other species were not even considered to be *Equus*. At one time the genus *Plesippus* was used for what are now considered the earliest species of *Equus*. The primitive anatomy of the skeleton of *Plesippus* provided a link between *Dinohippus*, the earlier ancestor, and *Equus*. Such was the case when the Smithsonian visited Hagerman in 1929. The Smithsonian paleontologist who first worked the site now known as the Smithsonian Horse Quarry was James W. Gidley, then the leading student of fossil horses. When Gidley first described the material from Hagerman, he named it *Plesippus shoshonensis* because of the animal's primitive skeletal structure. Later researchers decided that Gidley's species from Hagerman was the same as the previously described *Equus simplicidens* from Texas.

Since many fossil species of *Equus* have often been described based on a single tooth, it has been difficult to determine if all these different species are really valid. If one species is based on an upper tooth and another on a lower, then can we really be sure they are distinct, or do the differences merely reflect the differences between upper and lower teeth? There are many factors that contribute to the variations we see in fossils. They may reflect the age of an individual or be indicative of the differences between males and females. What makes the Smithsonian Horse Quarry sample so important is that it represents a large sample of a single species; it includes males, females, and individuals of all different ages. This site provides a paleontologist with the opportunity to examine the range of variation present in a species. Such a site is a rare occurrence in a fossil record that often consists of bits and pieces rather than whole skulls or skeletons.

Zebralike *Equus* first appeared 3.7 million years ago during the Pliocene. Left: Grevy's zebra stallions battle for dominance. Previous: excavating the Horse Quarry.

The science of paleontology is constantly reexamining the available fossil evidence, proposing hypotheses regarding the ecology or relationships of extinct animals based on that evidence, and then testing each hypothesis as new evidence becomes available. A hypothesis on the ecology of an extinct species will be weak when only isolated bones and teeth are available. When a large sample of individuals such as that of the Hagerman Horse from the Smithsonian Quarry becomes available, an earlier hypothesis may be strengthened, or as is often the case, revised. Such a large sample provides an opportunity to gain a wealth of information that might not be otherwise possible to glean from the fossil record. Studies of the skeleton of the Hagerman Horse from this sample, and comparison with its modern living relatives, suggest that it is actually more zebralike than horselike. More specifically, its skull, teeth, and skeleton are most similar to the living Grevy's zebra, which inhabits arid regions in the northern part of Africa.

Epochs of *Equus*

Holocene
Present.
Horses return to America.

Pleistocene
2 mya.
Horses roam North America. *Equus* buried in Hagerman deposits.

Pliocene
5 mya.
Three-toed horse types spread south across the Panamanian Isthmus.

Miocene
17 mya.
An epoch of diversification. Merychippus , a grazer, appears among browsing horses. Apelike humans forage near wooded Tuscany.

Oligocene
33 mya.
Early apes, primitive mastodons, shallow-jawed *Miohippus* horses.

Eocene
55 mya.
Hyracotherium, or "Dawn Horse," the first *equid.*

Paleocene
65 mya.
Extinction of dinosaurs.

Some horse experts consider Grevy's zebra the most primitive of the living members of the horse family, so some of the features shared with the Hagerman Horse may reflect the generally more primitive skeletal structure of Grevy's zebra. One of the features they have in common is a long skull with a

Strange Beasts

Exclusive to North America, *Oreodonts* combined characteristics of camels, deer, and pigs. Their most extraordinary and specialized member, *Pronomotherium*, appeared in the late Miocene exhibiting the kind of bizarre changes often found in the family. Its exaggerated proboscis masked a skull similar to great apes. About the size of a wild boar, it lived in large herds and shared grassy plains with early horses.

prominent occipital region, the back of the skull where the neck muscles attach. Also, the folds of enamel on the lower molar teeth are similar. Like modern zebras, the Hagerman Horse has a small hoof in proportion to its body size. While the horse was larger than its ancient ancestors, it was not an especially large animal. Slightly smaller than today's zebras, it stood about 4.3 feet (13 hands) at the shoulder. Some of its descendants are larger, but not all. The living donkey is smaller than the Hagerman Horse.

Like all modern members of the family *Equidae*, Hagerman's *Equus simplicidens* was one-toed with reduced side toes. The middle toe supported all the animal's weight. This adaptation to running had already occurred earlier, so *Equus* was not the only one-toed horse. It merely continued the trend, with the remnant splints of the side toes completely hidden beneath the skin. The main bones for support in the hand and feet (metacarpal and metatarsal) continued to become elongated, increasing the overall length. Longer legs meant a longer stride and more ground covered. "In the horse," paleontologist W. B. Scott said, "everything has been sacrificed to speed, making the animal a '"cursorial machine."'"

Perhaps one of the most telling features of the skeleton in this early ancestor of modern horses is the upper leg bone, or humerus. One of the very distinct characteristics of living horses is their ability to stand, even sleep, upright for long periods of time. This is possible because of a specialized system of muscles, ligaments, and deep fascia (a connective tissue) known as the stay-apparatus. This serves to transfer the role of supporting body weight from active muscles to non-fatiguing structures in the skeleton of the fore and hind limbs. How can we tell that the Hagerman Horse had this stay-apparatus? Although muscles, ligaments, and fascia all quickly decay after the death of the animal and are not preserved as fossils, these tissues have to attach to bones. They often leave some type of mark, such as ridges and muscle scars, that allows paleontologists to establish their existence. In modern horses there is an extra ridge of bone on the humerus near the shoulder joint that shows where a ligament associated with the passive stay-apparatus attached. This ridge is

absent in earlier horses and suggests that they could not stand for long periods or sleep standing upright like modern horses. The earliest horse with a well-developed ridge and hence a well-developed stay-apparatus is *Equus simplicidens*, the Hagerman Horse, and this feature is present in all its living descendants.

What is the importance of this particular anatomical feature? Modern horses are grazers and feed primarily on grasses. Grasses are not as nutritionally rich as other plants, so grazing is not very efficient and requires large amounts of food to be ingested. Grazing horses, in contrast to earlier browsing horses, spend a lot of time standing and feeding in open country in full view of potential predators. The stay-apparatus is one way an animal can conserve muscular energy so that it is available for running and escape should the need arise. Any anatomical feature that aids in escaping predators certainly contributes to the survival of the species.

Being a grazer can be rough on the teeth. Grasses contain little bits of the mineral silica, which has the same composition as quartz sand or glass. These little bits of silica, called phytoliths or literally plant-stones, act as the skeleton of the grass blades.

Cutting Edges Keep Pace with Faster Feet

Horses are classified by the structure of their teeth and arrangement of their limbs— how they eat and move. Of the four tooth types, molars tell the most. Molar crowns grew taller and tougher to adapt to grazing grasses containing abrasive silica. Distinct cusp patterns with zig-zag and cutting edge projections differentiated horse types and helped them become efficient grazing machines. Horses changed from the browsing to the grazing lifestyle by gradually abandoning flat-footed, four-toed feet for raised, action-ready, single-toed feet. This new set of feet plus longer legs made horses into efficient running machines.

Any animal, like a horse, chewing these grasses also has to chew bits of silica, resulting in rapid wear of the teeth. How does an animal deal with such an abrasive diet? There are three possible solutions. First, have a tooth that is ever-growing so that even as the tooth is being worn down, more new tooth is being formed. This approach is found in rodents; their front teeth or incisors are used for gnawing and hence are rapidly worn down. For animals that do not have ever-growing teeth, an alternative is to have taller teeth in which the crown, the "business" part of the tooth, takes longer to wear down. The third solution is to have tougher teeth. Teeth are made primarily of two parts, the harder enamel and a softer dentine, better known as ivory. Animals that eat plants have teeth with a chewing surface formed by alternating ridges of enamel and dentine. The difference in hardness produces low and high areas that trap and hold plants and then cut them. Those animals that eat more abrasive food have more complex ridges of enamel that form a greater proportion of the chewing surface so that it takes longer to wear down. Another way a tooth becomes tougher is by the addition of a third substance, cementum, to the outside of the tooth to make it stronger. While cementum is harder than dentine, it is not as hard as enamel. Yet it does aid in helping the tooth withstand abrasive food.

Hyaenodon differed from carnivores with its smaller brain and foot bones that allowed only its toes to touch the ground. Probably not fast enough to hunt horses, it scavenged them in North America, Asia, and Africa from the Eocene to the Miocene. Right: Pliocene flora and fauna in the Hagerman Valley about four million years ago.

Which of these adaptations to making the teeth withstand an abrasive diet is present in the Hagerman Horse? All of them. Horses had become grazers long before *Equus*, so the development of high-crowned (hypsodont) teeth for grazing occurred much earlier in the evolution of the horse, though it is best developed in *Equus*. The permanent teeth also grow longer because there is a delay in the development of roots. Once the roots form, there is no longer any new tooth material produced, and from then on the crown of the tooth is slowly worn away. The teeth of *Equus* have a more complex folding of the enamel than is seen in the teeth of its ancestors; they also have cementum, so the tooth does not wear down as quickly.

While we can study horse skeletons, their skin, muscles, and other soft tissues are only preserved under extraordinary conditions such as freezing or mummification. Without skin we have no way of knowing whether the Hagerman Horse had stripes like the modern zebra.

Stripes provide protection against predators, a useful adaptation in a herd animal. Since there is evidence that the Hagerman Horse did form herds or at least extended family

groups, reconstructing the animal with stripes seems legitimate. But without preserved skin, we cannot say for sure.

Primeval Landscapes

Since Cope's discovery in 1892, paleontologists have identified *Equus simplicidens* at forty-seven sites ranging from Idaho to California and South Dakota to Mexico. The variety of environments found within this broad region today makes it safe to imagine that the number of possible habitats in this area also existed in the past. It certainly suggests that the Hagerman Horse was flexible in its habits and adaptable to a variety of environments.

In order to fully understand the ecology of the Hagerman Horse, a thorough knowledge of all the fossil sites where it is found is necessary. Although Hagerman is only one of many sites, it does provide the best record of the environment in which *Equus simplicidens* lived.

Hagerman can be thought of as the keystone to our understanding of this species based on two different criteria. The first one has already been mentioned: the large sample of *Equus simplicidens* found at the Smithsonian Horse Quarry. The second is the rich fossil preserve

from the Hagerman site of the many other different species of vertebrates, invertebrates, and plants that shared the environment with the Hagerman Horse when it was alive. While all the other sites may also preserve the flora and fauna, none can compare in the number and diversity of species found. As a result of the work started at Hagerman in 1929 by the Smithsonian and continuing with the work done by numerous other researchers up to the present, 111 species of vertebrates, thirty-nine species of invertebrates, and thirty-four species of plants have been documented. Thus the Hagerman area represents the best-known record of life for the Pliocene (4.8 to 1.9 million years ago) in North America.

In addition to its variety of fossil plants and animals, Hagerman has an added bonus preserved in the bluffs that overlook the Snake River: volcanic ashes. Geologically speaking, the eruption of a volcano and the deposition of volcanic ash on the landscape is an instantaneous event. Each type of volcanic ash has its own distinctive chemistry, reflecting the local rocks that were melted down and blown out of the volcano. This unique fingerprint allows us to match ash layers from the same volcanic eruption to determine that widely separated rock layers were formed at the same time.

Not only does the ash allow geologists to show a similar age for different rocks, but in some cases they can even determine exactly when the volcano erupted and deposited that ash layer. Some volcanic ashes similar to the type that came out of Mount St. Helens are rich in the element potassium. Some of the potassium is a radioactive isotope that decays into the inert gas argon. When the volcano erupts, any argon gas present escapes from the hot rock into the air so that when the volcanic ash settles onto the landscape there is no argon present. As time passes, new argon is produced by the decay of the radioactive potassium and remains trapped in the crystals of the minerals in the ash. Since the rate of change from radioactive potassium to argon is constant, there is an increase in the amount of argon present: the more argon present, the older the ash layer. This radiometric clock is the method by which the age of the rocks can be determined.

There are two very distinctive ash layers at Hagerman, and based on their chemical fingerprint we can tell that they came from two very different areas. The older of these two ashes is called the Peters Gulch Ash and was named for the site where it was originally dis-

The flood-carved Snake River Canyon at Hagerman where irrigated farms top fossil-rich bluffs. Left: Hagerman's *Equus simplicidens*.

covered, Peters Gulch, in the southern part of Hagerman Fossil Beds National Monument. Its chemical composition shows this ash originated from a volcano in what is now the Yellowstone area. The age of this ash has been determined to be about 3.7 million years old. While in most places the Peters Gulch Ash forms only a thin layer, in a few places it is almost three feet thick where it washed into ponds on the Hagerman landscape. The surface of the ash has ripple marks reflecting water movement in the pond. Higher up in the layers at Hagerman is another prominent ash layer known as the Fossil Gulch Ash. Fossil Gulch is also found within the monument and is located near the Smithsonian Horse Quarry. Unlike the Peters Gulch Ash, the Fossil Gulch Ash came from the west and probably was produced by a volcano somewhere along the Pacific coast. The exact spot has not yet been identified. It has been dated at 3.2 million years. Since the sediments at Hagerman go below the Peters Gulch Ash and above the Fossil Gulch Ash, we can safely assume that the 600-feet-high bluffs span more than the 500,000 years represented between the two ash layers.

What can we say about life in the Hagerman area between 3.7 and 3.2 million years ago? Based on the plant pollen found preserved in some sediments, southern Idaho 3.5 million years ago was wetter than it is today, with about twice as much annual precipitation. The greater amount of annual precipitation reaching southern Idaho at this time was probably due to the lower elevation of the Coast and Cascade Ranges to the west. Today these mountain ranges capture much of the moisture coming in from the Pacific and create a rain shadow. However, 3.5 million years ago they had not yet been pushed to their present height, so moisture from the Pacific Ocean reached farther inland. This greater amount of moisture permitted many types of trees such as pine, fir, spruce, juniper, hemlock, and false hemlock, which today are found at higher elevations, to grow on the Snake River Plain where sagebrush now dominates. In many places there were woodlands or somewhat open forest. Along the rivers the riparian vegetation included willow, alder, birch, and elm.

Cross-bedding, overlapping, and sloped sand layers deposited by ancient rivers are common. Like the present-day Salmon Falls Creek, Bruneau River, and Owyhee River, the rivers passing through the Hagerman area originated in Nevada and flowed north. Unlike their modern counterparts, these rivers did not empty into the Snake River that runs by the monument today, since it would not be formed until a million years later. The rivers passing through the Hagerman area emptied into a large lake to the west known as Lake Idaho. While the size of Lake Idaho fluctuated in response to changes in climate, at its largest it was about the size of Lake Ontario. Drainage from Lake Idaho was across Oregon and into northern California. This is known because the nearest living relatives of species of the fish, freshwater snails, and clams unique to the lake are found in the Sacramento Valley today.

Equus thrived on the Pliocene grasslands. Left: saber-toothed *Smilodon fatalis*, a horse predator, used its curved canines to slash the throat or belly of an animal after ambushing it. The dramatic teeth might also have served for social display, like antlers.

Predators and Prey

Many of the sediments present at Hagerman indicate the presence of wetlands. In the middle part of the Glenns Ferry Formation exposed at Hagerman, ancient pond deposits are common. These are represented by finely layered, brown shales rich in organic material contributed by decaying plants such as cattails. The presence of extensive wetlands is also reflected in the fauna. A variety of frogs is known from Hagerman, as well as a salamander. While no turtles live in the Snake River or its tributaries today, at the time of the Hagerman Horse the fauna included two types of turtles. Most of the birds known from Hagerman are waterfowl. Ducks, geese, swans, pelicans, cormorants, ibis, four types of grebes, herons, and rails were all present. Common mammals included two types of beaver, an otter, and the ancestor to the living muskrat.

The environment at Hagerman was not restricted to wetlands. Savannah grassland habitat was also present, and in addition to the variety of animals associated with wetlands, the Hagerman fauna has species like the horse that would have inhabited more open country. While the various ponds, streams, and rivers would have been important water sources for the Hagerman Horse, its preferred habitat would have been these open grasslands. Sharing the grasslands with the horse were peccaries, a New World relative of the pig, along with llamas, camels, and antelope. None of these grassland species were as common as the wetland forms, suggesting that during part of the time when sediments were being deposited at

Hagerman, open grasslands were not yet as extensive as they eventually became. Smaller mammals in that open country included gophers, ground squirrels, and perhaps one or two types of rabbits. The birds present in this more open country included a burrowing owl.

The first abundant grass pollen found at Hagerman is high in the layers, at about the same level as the Horse Quarry. While horses were present in the Hagerman fauna earlier, they were not common. Perhaps the earlier wetland habitat was only marginally used by the species, and only with the drying of the climate and spread of grasslands did horses become common in the area so that a site with a high concentration of grassland species like the Horse Quarry could be formed.

In any ecosystem there are prey and there are predators. One of the outstanding features of the fauna at Hagerman was the variety of carnivores present: thirteen species. They ranged in size from a weasel to a small sabertooth cat. Only the sabertooth cat and the hyenalike dog were large enough to prey on the Hagerman Horse. Two types of dogs were present. The ancestral coyote, like its modern descendant, probably fed on rabbits and mice, both of which were abundant. The other dog, *Borophagus*, belonged to an extinct group. Much like the modern hyena, it was adapted to crushing bones, making it a likely predator of the Hagerman Horse. The Hagerman fauna also included an early ancestor of the black bear that, like its descendant, had flat crushing teeth, indicating it, too, was probably an omnivore. While it may have scavenged carcasses of dead horses, it probably did not actively pursue them.

Plaster-casted fossil specimen from the Hagerman Horse Quarry.

Toward the top of the bluffs at Hagerman is the Smithsonian Horse Quarry. It seems to have formed at a time when there was a decrease in the amount of wetlands, for there are no carbonaceous shales representing ponds this high in the bluffs. Water was still present, as the quarry itself was formed in the bed of an ancient river.

As the mountain ranges to the west uplifted, the landscape became more arid and the woodlands declined, with grasses becoming increasingly prominent. The continuing success of the horse as it diversified and evolved into new species reflected its adaptations to this open grassland environment.

While the Smithsonian Horse Quarry is an important site, it is not the only place in the Monument where horse remains are found. As with much of the fauna, most other finds of fossil horses consist of isolated bones and teeth. This is not surprising since vertebrate skeletons are easily scattered following the death of an animal; finding a fairly complete skeleton is a rare event. Even more rare is the discovery of large concentrations of numerous individuals of a single species. Although a single tooth or bone can provide important information about an extinct species, it is only when a large sample is studied that we can gain significant insight into the lifestyles and habits of a species. Such a sample allows paleontologists to assess the range of variation within a species. How large are the largest individuals, and how small are the smallest? Is its size related to the sex or age of an individual, and what are the important differences that distinguish one species from another? When working with an often fragmentary fossil record, such information is important for determining if a find really represents a new type of animal or merely an extreme version of a previously known species. One of C. L. Gazin's early studies on the Smithsonian Horse Quarry sample looked at some of these questions.

Large samples can originate in two very different ways, and the resulting samples each provide different types of information about the species. Some samples result from long-term, gradual accumulations in one spot. The famous tar pits at Rancho La Brea in Los Angeles, California, are a classic example. They record changes over a long period of time, biologically speaking. Other accumulations are formed more quickly as the result of a catastrophic event that "freezes" in time a snapshot of what the living population was like. The causes of these catastrophic accumulations are varied and can range from floods and droughts to volcanic eruptions or disease.

One type of important information that can be gleaned from a large sample of animals killed in a flood, drought, or other catastrophic event is the herd's population structure. Such a sample provides an opportunity to see the number of individuals of different age classes and the ratio of the sexes in these groups. The question is whether there are clear ways to determine the age of individuals and if there are features of the skull or skeleton that permit us to tell males from females. Fortunately the close similarity between the Hagerman Horse and its modern relatives gives paleontologists important clues.

Fossil sleuth Bob Willhite examines an emerging horse skeleton.

One very quick and simple way to identify a male horse using either the skull or jaw is to look at the canine, also known as the eye tooth. In stallions this tooth is large and well developed. In mares the tooth is much smaller and in many individuals absent. In modern horses younger than about three years, this tooth has not erupted and is therefore not a useful feature in the very young. About the time young stallions start to become sexually mature, this tooth erupts and becomes visible, thus making determination of the sex of the individual easy.

Horses, like many other mammals, have two sets of teeth, deciduous and permanent. We can observe at what age an animal gets its deciduous teeth, when these teeth are shed, and when each of the permanent teeth are in place. Since this information is available for domestic horses and wild horses such as zebras, we can then determine the age of a

Hagerman Horse fossil by looking for a similar pattern of tooth eruption and which teeth are in place.

Determining the age of a mammal is not restricted to looking at the teeth. Many bones of the skeleton start out as separate centers of bone formation. As an animal grows and matures, many of these centers fuse together. Different bones fuse at different times in an animal's life. What we know about bone formation in modern horses helps researchers profile the herd uncovered at the Hagerman site.

One of the early explanations for the large number of individuals at the Smithsonian Horse Quarry was that they had gathered at a water hole. It was thought that over the years as animals came to the water hole, some died and became buried. As the remains accumulated, a large number of animals became preserved at the site. If this explanation for the origin of the site was correct, then it should be reflected in the age distribution of the animals preserved. In gradual accumulations such as this, the individuals most likely to die are the very young and very old. Both are more vulnerable than prime adults to any predators also likely to be found around the water hole. Other possible causes of death might be entrapment in the mud, since these animals might be too weak to escape. Looking at the skulls and jaws, a sample composed of individuals with milk teeth and individuals with heavily worn permanent teeth should be evident.

A study of the age of the animals from the quarry demonstrated that not only were very young and very old individuals present but also all ages in between. The sample did not fit the expected pattern of a gradual accumulation but rather a catastrophic one in which individuals of all ages were killed. While this new information does not provide any explanation as to how the animals died, it certainly suggests that they died within a relatively short time of each other.

Guarding the Harem

Some species of mammals have a reproductive strategy of breeding throughout the year. Others breed seasonally once a year. The Hagerman Horse may have bred seasonally since many of the skulls found in the Smithsonian quarry sample have teeth at the same stage of development and wear. Modern Burchell's zebras living in Africa have a similar age structure to the Hagerman population. They breed once a year and births peak during the wet season when food availability is optimal. The type of vegetation present at Hagerman based on the pollen record suggests that during the Pliocene the annual rainfall was twenty inches a year, with most of it restricted to the winter season. It is not unreasonable to infer that the breeding of the Hagerman Horse was probably closely tied to this seasonal rainfall.

Females in the sample are better represented than males by a ratio of 1.4:1 based on skulls and 2.2:1 based on jaws. These sex ratios are similar to those in the living Burchell's zebra. Burchell's zebra, like many other wild *equids*, has a social organization composed of two groups: a reproductive group of a dominant stallion with a number of mares and their young, and separate bands of bachelor males. The pattern in the Horse Quarry sample suggests that the Hagerman Horse had a social structure similar to that of Burchell's zebra. Zebra bachelor and breeding bands tend to remain separate, and the dominant male is most defensive of his harem while the mares are reproductively receptive. However, since breeding only occurs once a year, the stallion does not have to actively guard his harem all year. In Africa many of these separate bands will come together for the seasonal migration in search of food when the dry season comes. As a result, there are times when hundreds of individuals will be concentrated in a small area. It is very possible that the Hagerman Horse had similar behavior, and that the large number of individuals preserved at the quarry represents portions of one of these migratory congregations of horses.

Modern wild horses descended from the domesticated stock brought to the American West by Spanish explorers over 400 years ago. Below: mustang mares with their foals. Left: Snake River petroglyph.

Although the idea of a catastrophic event killing a large number of horses sounds plausible as an explanation for the origin of the Smithsonian Horse Quarry, we still need to seek evidence that will support this interpretation. While we have looked at the biological evidence of the animals themselves, there is another important source of information. Geological evidence includes the types of sediments in which the horses were buried and how the bones of the horses were positioned within these sediments.

Sediments at the Horse Quarry reveal the presence of moving water. If the site was a water hole as originally thought, then the pattern of sediment deposition would show very fine-grained particles that settled out in quiet water.

As these particles settled to the bottom of the water hole, we might expect to see distinct layers formed, except perhaps near the edge where they would be disturbed by animals

A juvenile Hagerman Horse jaw overlays a mare's in a rare proximity.

walking around. Recent studies of the sediments of the Horse Quarry indicate that the bone layer sits on the bottom of an ancient riverbed. The lowest sediments are the coarsest, including small balls of clay ripped up from the bottom of the channel. From these coarse sediments the particles get smaller in the higher levels above the base of the channel. This pattern of going from coarse to finer sediments indicates a slowing down of the water flow. The finer sediments also display a pattern called cross-bedding in which the layers form crescent patterns. Because the size of sediment particles and the pattern of cross-bedding vary depending on the depth and speed of the water, we can reconstruct the type of river in which the bones were buried. The shape of the ancient river suggests that this was a fairly straight channel that did not meander. The water was slow, moving less then three feet per second, and shallow, less than twenty inches. These were certainly not conditions that could trap, drown, and bury a herd of animals similar in size to the living zebra.

Very few complete skeletons have been found. Of the more than 200 individuals collected since 1929, only about eight are represented by fairly complete skeletons. Although there are thousands of horse bones in this one small area, they tend to be scattered and isolated. This is not to say that parts of skeletons did not stay together; often skulls and jaws are still attached, and occasional strings of vertebrae are found. Usually when bones are found in place still in their original anatomical connections, they are from the lower legs such as the wrist and ankle. Had the Smithsonian Horse Quarry formed when a large number of individuals drowned in a flood, then their quick burial should have resulted in mostly complete skeletons instead of scattered bones. Any explanation for the origin of the quarry needs to look at two different events: what killed the animals, and what caused their bones to accumulate in a small area on the bottom of an ancient riverbed.

Why They Died

Since few articulated skeletons are found in the quarry, it is safe to assume that enough time passed between the death of the animals to allow their carcasses to rot enough for bones to become separated. Once a bone becomes exposed, it will start to weather and undergo a distinctive pattern of decomposition as the organic part decays. While some skulls are broken in such a way that they may have been stepped on, the surface of most bones does not show any type of weathering that would suggest they sat exposed to the elements for long periods of time. They were probably exposed less than a year before being buried. If we consider the anatomy of a horse and the relationship of bones to muscles, it is quickly obvious that the lower part of the legs does not have much muscle. The skin covers a few tendons, but that is about all that is present. After the animal dies, the skin dries and shrinks, forming a tight package that holds the bones of the wrist and ankle in place. In other parts of the body, such as the upper parts of the leg where there are more muscles to decompose, it is easier for the bones to become separated. The above pattern only applies to an animal that dies on dry land, not in water. An animal submerged in water would have its soft tissues quickly decay so that all of the skeleton would become separated.

How bones are transported in a moving current depends on their size and shape and the speed of the water. Horses have about 205 bones in their skeleton, ranging in size from the largest like the skull, jaws, and hips to the smallest such as the wrist and ankle bones or those in the tail. By measuring the compass direction of the long bones of the leg we can determine if the current helped align the bones in a preferred orientation. Measurements of the long axis of the troughs in the cross-bedded sands show that the current flowed from northeast to southwest. Therefore, there should be a pattern of two sets of bone orientation. One set of bones would align with the current and a second set with the bones positioned at right angles. This pattern is not present in the Horse Quarry bone assemblage. Although there is some indication that many bones were rolling with the current, it was not strong enough to sort the long bones into two groups oriented at right angles to each other.

Because all bones of the skeleton are present and the water current was too weak to remove small bones or move larger bones into the typical bimodal pattern of orientation, we can conclude two things. Where the bones are buried is close to where the animals died, and the bones were not washed downstream from someplace else. If river current cannot account for the large number of bones deposited at the quarry, then why are so many horse skeletons concentrated in one spot? The idea that there was a large number of animals due to a seasonal migration has been proposed, but the evidence shows the river was neither deep nor fast enough to cause drowning. Also, if the bones were not transported any great distance, then the carcasses most likely decomposed in the river bottom before the water rose. Therefore, the animals did not likely die adjacent to the river.

Although many kinds of catastrophes kill herd animals, the explanation that best fits the Hagerman data is catastrophic drought. The summers on the Snake River Plain during the Pliocene were cooler and the winters were warmer than those of today. The average temperature during the late fall, winter, and early spring did not extend below 10°C (50°F). If rainfall was seasonal and mostly fell during the winter, then any delay or reduction in rain might have a dramatic effect on the river. If the river was as broad and shallow as the geology suggests, it would have dried up quickly. The river may have already been at its lowest at the end of the dry summer season. Excavations at the quarry show there were low areas that would have

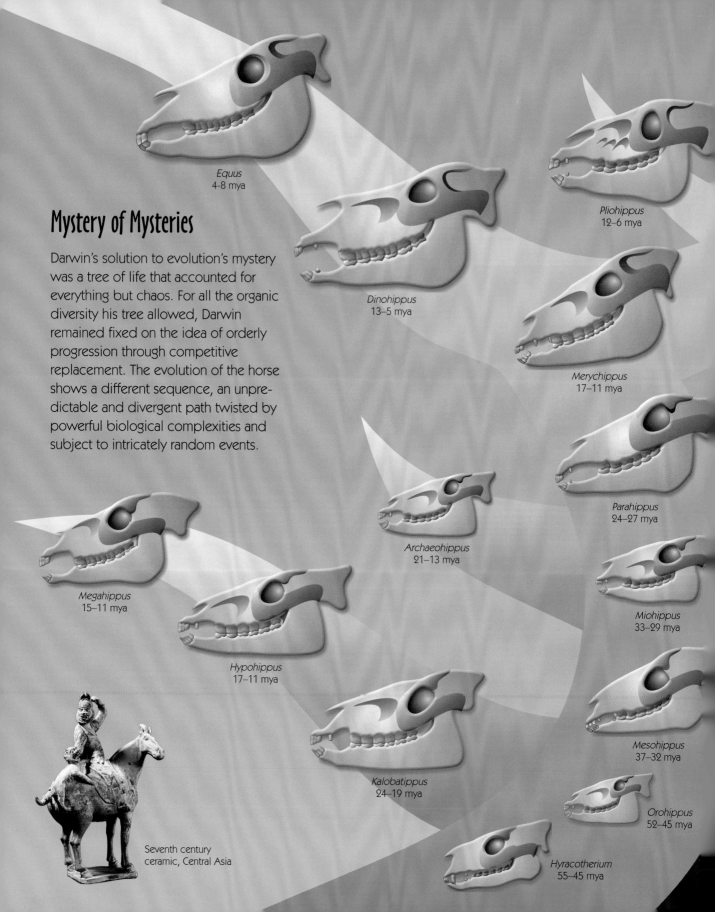

Mystery of Mysteries

Darwin's solution to evolution's mystery was a tree of life that accounted for everything but chaos. For all the organic diversity his tree allowed, Darwin remained fixed on the idea of orderly progression through competitive replacement. The evolution of the horse shows a different sequence, an unpredictable and divergent path twisted by powerful biological complexities and subject to intricately random events.

Equus
4–8 mya

Dinohippus
13–5 mya

Pliohippus
12–6 mya

Merychippus
17–11 mya

Archaeohippus
21–13 mya

Parahippus
24–27 mya

Megahippus
15–11 mya

Hypohippus
17–11 mya

Miohippus
33–29 mya

Kalobatippus
24–19 mya

Mesohippus
37–32 mya

Orohippus
52–45 mya

Hyracotherium
55–45 mya

Seventh century
ceramic, Central Asia

Hippidion
2 mya–10,000
years ago

Neohipparion
16–5 mya

been deep pools, and these may have held small amounts of water even after most of the river had disappeared.

All living horses are water-dependent. Dominant stallions of Grevy's zebra select and defend territories with the best water and food supplies in the arid parts of Africa. Burchell's zebras have a seasonal migration to areas with water and plants when the dry season comes. There is no reason to think that the Hagerman Horse was any different in its physiology. If the animal's foaling season was tied to the yearly rains, then any delay in those rains would have a severe effect on the population. If it was the beginning of the foaling season and the winter rains had not yet arrived, then mares would have been drawn to any remaining water and edible riparian plants. The presence of skeletons of young horses only weeks old in the quarry suggests that death occurred at this time. The high concentration of horses around the last remnants of water in the dried riverbed probably depleted the remaining vegetation. Horses then died from either starvation or thirst as the last pools of water and available vegetation disappeared. The result would have been a dried riverbed littered with horse carcasses. Eventually the riverbed refilled with water, either with the arrival of late rains of the season or perhaps with the next season's rainfall. There was enough of a time lag that carcasses had decomposed sufficiently to scatter loose bones about the riverbed. As the river filled, bones were moved some and then buried, resulting in the deposit seen today. Although only one species of *Equus* was present at Hagerman three million years ago, by 2.5 million years ago we can recognize multiple species that are descendants.

A fourteenth century terra-cotta equestrian from the Mali region of West Africa. Below: bronze of French emperor Charlemagne, about A.D. 800. Right: Hagerman's herd may have died from starvation or thirst at a shrinking water hole.

Equus Survives

Shortly after the appearance of *Equus simplicidens*, the species diversified and evolved. Even though we think of this species as being "extinct," it is not a true extinction but rather a reflection of its success at adapting to the changing environment by evolving into new species. By the end of the Pliocene, fossil localities from Texas to Idaho have more than one species of *Equus*. Not only did *Equus simplicidens* evolve into new species, but its descendants dispersed and moved into new habitats. This took place across the North American continent and also into Asia and Europe. The earliest record of *Equus* in Asia and Europe is about 2.6 million years old. *Equus* finally entered Africa about 1.9 million years ago, where it is found in Kenya and Ethiopia. African zebras are descended from these pioneers.

Dispersal of *Equus* was not limited to Asia, Europe, and Africa; it was also part of the faunal interchange between North and South America along with llamas, tapirs, and peccaries. About 500,000 years ago, *Equus* crossed the Isthmus of Panama into South America. Remains of *Equus* are widespread on the continent and have been found on the pampas of Argentina, in caves in Brazil, and in tar pits in Peru and Ecuador. By the end of the Ice Age, *Equus* had become extinct there just as its

relatives in North America also became extinct. The question of why the horse disappeared in South America after being successful for half a million years is just as much a mystery as its disappearance from North America, the continent of its origin.

An admirable running machine, *Equus* adapted not only to open country but a variety of environments. Its descendants have occupied all the world's continents except Australia and Antarctica. An efficient grazer, the horse processed vegetation avoided by other herbivores. Social behavior and a close bond between man and horse may have helped the Hagerman lineage survive, yet the rapid spread of humanity also restricts equine habitat.

Horses such as the quagga are now extinct. Grevy's zebra, Przewalski's horse, and the

Extremely adaptable, horses also have a cooperative herd nature that makes for strong bonding with humans, a survival bonus in diminishing habitats. Cowboy Dennis Avery begins an alliance on his Bruneau, Idaho, ranch.

Somalian ass are considered endangered species. The modern threat to equine survival is unprecedented. Industry, agriculture, and other human-induced ecological transformations have accelerated the rate of change beyond the capacity of the animals to adapt. We can only hope that our activities can be modified so that the descendants of the Hagerman Horse will survive to amaze, intrigue, and delight future generations.

◆

Kelly A. Murphey, M.A.
Hagerman Fossil Beds National Monument
Kathryn Baxter, M.A.
History, Boise State University

Arrows and Atlatls

CHAPTER THREE

Buhla was 5´ 2˝ and 10,675 years old. Nellis Burkhart found her in a gravel quarry near Buhl on a brisk January morning in 1989. Sifting rock and sand through a rock crusher's screen for the highway department, foreman Burkhart spotted a bone. He headed back to the bank where the front-end loader had last dug and discovered more bones stuck in the fragile bar, with others loose in the dirt displaced by the loader. The next day, Burkhart's wife, Loretta, showed some of the bones to her colleague at Buhl Middle School, science teacher Marvin Barosovsky. He said they were human, and Loretta Burkhart called the Herrett Museum in Twin Falls the next morning.

The Buhl highway department crew handed off the loose bones they had collected to archaeologists from the Herrett Museum and the Idaho State Historical Society. The scientists

"Buhla," an Archaic woman as imagined by artist Bill West. Right: carved elk antler quirt with leather whip and wrist strap, evidence of the return of the horse to Idaho in the 1700s. Previous: the Camas Prairie, named for the starchy bulbs that once sustained southcentral Idaho nomads. "The blue lake of camas blossoms presents a picture never to be forgotten," wrote pioneer Lucy M. Nelson in 1937.

saw they had to move fast. The Bonneville Flood gravel bar where Buhla lay had begun to collapse as the soil on top thawed in the winter sun. Also, Buhla was drawing an interested crowd. Ducking boulders and frozen dirt chunks, the excavators pulled a mandible, cranium, ribs, and vertebrae from the crumbling quarry face, then screened the dirt at the base for other bones and artifacts. It fell to state archaeologist Tom Green to enforce Idaho's 1984 Graves Protection Act by notifying the Fort Hall Shoshone-Bannock Tribal Council. Buhla was discovered on their traditional territory, and Green needed Sho-Ban permission for radiocarbon dating.

Buhla is one of the most complete and best-preserved Paleo-Indian skeletons ever recovered in North or South America. Her features resemble American Indian or East Asian people. She lived in a hunter-gatherer society when the receding glaciers of the last Ice Age made a cool, wet environment. Bison, elephants, and camels shared the Snake River Plain. Between 17 and 21 years old when she died, Buhla appeared healthy except for 15 episodes of arrested growth that affected her development, probably from stresses like seasonal lack of food or illness. She ate mostly deer, elk, bison, and small game animals, and occasionally the anadromous fish that returned from the ocean to spawn in the Snake River. Her people processed these meats into pemmican and made tailored leather clothes from hides. Someone buried Buhla with a brand new obsidian stemmed point under her head, an unused bone needle with a fine eye, a notched bone ornament, and a badger's baculum.

Old as Dirt

Buhla's bones and artifacts reveal detailed information about the people who lived in Idaho 12,000 years ago or longer. Paleoindian sites nearby on the Snake River Plain at Wilson Butte Cave, the Simon cache, the Wasden site, and Kelvin's Cave are some of the best evidence archaeologists have of a remarkable human migration. "This is an old burial," said geologist Bruce Cochrane, a grave even older than the carbon dating suggests. According to Cochrane, the method used tends to give young dates. He placed Buhla shortly after the Bonneville Flood, between 13,900 and 16,700 years ago. Archaeologists still work to establish which century people first arrived in the area. A few recoveries from rock shelters and caves, a few scraps of bone, stone, and charcoal may support a Pre-Archaic age of 14,000 to 15,000 years ago, dates certainly known elsewhere in the Americas. However, most regional archaeologists are more comfortable with evidence that dates from 3,000 to 4,000 years younger. A number of recoveries from southern Idaho, eastern Oregon, and western Utah place native people in a variety of settings between 11,000 and 10,000 years B.P. (before the present).

While the Snake River Plain's Native Americans might best be described as expert hunters of desert big game, small game, and fowl, their cultural history is far more complicated. They were also accomplished gatherers and collectors of dozens of edible and medicinal plants, insects, and pollens. And they developed into perhaps the greatest of all fishermen within the Great Basin culture area. The exact make-up of the local food economy, the design of the various living and food procurement structures, and particularly the character of the tools saw both dramatic change and subtle developments over time. Shifts also occurred in exactly where the locals and their visitors chose to reside on the terrain. The moister, cooler climate between 11,500 and 7,500 B.P. makes it difficult to predict where the archaeological evidence of that age might occur. Many ancient remains seem to correlate to higher terraces, extinct bogs/marshes, ephemeral streams, small springs, and to now-changed vegetation margins/zones. Today's riverside landscape usually proves to be misleading when trying to predict the presence of ancient camp or ambush sites.

The earliest recognized local evidence represents a variant of the Clovis culture. These people made several types of large "fluted" projectile points, known as Clovis points, and other beautifully crafted stone and bone tools. Their most common food association was mammoth. The Simon collection, one of the best-known Clovis collections in America, was unearthed on Camas Prairie. The Clovis culture's chronological successor, the Folsom culture, had its own characteristic fluted point and a strong preference for big-game hunting, especially the giant bison. Isolated Clovis spear points have already been found in the desert and on an elevated river terrace near Twin Falls. Several isolated Folsom points have also been found in the desert to the south and on river terraces located downstream near the western edge of the Snake River Plain. The best evidence for either a Clovis or a Folsom occupation in the vicinity comes from just a few miles upstream near Crystal Springs, where construction work exposed a classic Clovis point and other fluted and nonfluted points among stone and bone tools. Late Clovis or early Folsom vintage people apparently used an upper terrace as a temporary campsite. Interestingly, the span of time from Clovis to Folsom marks the approximate era that many of the megafauna species such as mastodon, ground sloth, and horse went extinct. Archaeological evidence does not exist to implicate humans as the cause of such extinctions, but they may have added to other environmental pressures.

Claw and clamshell necklace. Left: Snake River below Shoshone Falls, a spearfishing site at the upper limit of salmon migration.

Far more common than Clovis and Folsom materials, stemmed spear points may have first derived from the Clovis culture. Or, the Clovis/Folsom and stemmed spear manufacturers may represent two contemporary but independent cultural traditions. People using stemmed spear tips inhabited small campsites and retooling stations in great numbers in the high desert country located just south of the Hagerman Fossil Beds. Their spear tips might indicate hunting or scouting of big game, perhaps as the prey entered the river valley for water or shelter.

The Archaic started shortly after 8,000 B.P. and saw settlement patterns expanded to include rock shelters, open camps, and various task-specific sites. The construction of thatched pit houses

Original extent

Before hunting for robes & hides

Range of the two great herds in 1870

Range of the southern herd in 1875

Range of the northern herd in 1880

Railroads

Stanley Mix, an artist with the 1855 Pacific Railroad Survey, captured the last of the northern herd. "On the western plain," said historian Wayne Gard, "the buffalo and the Indian were linked as closely as they would be later on a nickel coin." Inset: monstrous *Bison latifrons* roamed a colder, wetter Idaho during the late Pleistocene.

demonstrates a noticeable move toward winter sedentism in the river valley. Elaborate cemeteries occurred with masses of grave goods on the far-western Snake River Plain between 5,900 and 3,400 B.P., but this complex pattern does not seem to have spread to the Middle Snake. Some of the caves found in the lava beds just south and east of Hagerman Valley indicate that Archaic Period people possessed a remarkably diverse tool kit, including chipped stone cutting, scraping, and piercing items, basketry, cordage, bone needles, antler ice picks, and various ground stone tools. They preferred camping on the north side of the river valley and successfully hunted mountain sheep, deer, bison, and elk with the aid of an ingenious spear thrower, the atlatl.

Written in Stone

A study of petroglyphs and pictographs conducted along this segment of the Snake River and in the desert just to the south suggests that petroglyphs emerged with hunting blinds, about 3,000 years ago or slightly earlier. Recent archaeological data from central to eastern Idaho and from eastern Oregon also suggest that the ancestors of the ethnographic Shoshone entered the area during the middle portion of the Archaic, about 4,000 to 3,500 B.P. Earlier suggestions had Shoshone entering the area 8,000 years ago or only about 1,000 years ago.

The absence of fishing tackle and salmon remains during most of the Archaic is puzzling. Salmon were plentiful enough to be taken in Hells Canyon by 7,190 to 7,250 years ago, and they provided some of the food base at Givens Hot Springs near Marsing by 4,200 years ago. However, salmon are not documented until far later elsewhere in the region.

During the Late Period 1,500 to 2,000 years ago, an exceptional technology emerged: the bow and arrow. The atlatl (spear thrower) had allowed hunters to hit a large target from thirty to fifty feet with considerable accuracy; the bow and arrow effectively doubled that range. The emergence of arrow points in the archaeological record marks a dramatic increase in the capability to select targets and successfully procure meat. Other hallmarks of the Late Period include flowerpot-shaped pottery, cache/storage pits (some stone and stone slab lined), small wikiup huts, and numerous types of other tools and decorative items.

A large petroglyph site located just a few miles upstream from the Hagerman Monument marks a popular big-game killing site from 2,000 to 808 B.P. Another petroglyph site located on the north side of Upper Salmon Falls may evidence a Shoshone ritual related to bringing or celebrating a year's first run of salmon at this major spearfishing site. Early in this

Birch Creek pictographs. Left: Middle Snake archaeological finds include pendant, bone awl, and Shoshone clay pot.

period, rock alignments—walls and blinds—start to occur on steep-sided peninsulas jutting out from the north canyon rim of Hagerman Valley. About 1,000 years ago, north-side fishing sites emerged near falls and rapids. By 600 to 700 years ago, dentalium shell from the coast evidenced this vicinity's participation in a vast trade network. Stone-gathering forays and subsistence trips taken to and from the south mountains should have often brought families near the Hagerman Fossil Beds on a major "ethnographic"-era trail leading north-south along the rim of Salmon Falls Creek.

The Snake River Shoshone fishing communities, already well established in the Hagerman Valley area about 700 years ago, often referred to themselves in contact with whites as Neme or Nievi, meaning "we the people." Talking of their past, they also described

themselves as the Agaiduka or Akaitikka (Salmon Eaters) and Pia agaidika (Big Salmon Eaters). Actually, the local Shoshone could select from hundreds of edible foods including insects, plants, mussels, birds, fish, and game. They learned to eat anything, but most of the time they did not have to. They liked to camp in places where they could take significant amounts and combinations of their favorite foods. Their houses showed more variety in shape than is typi-

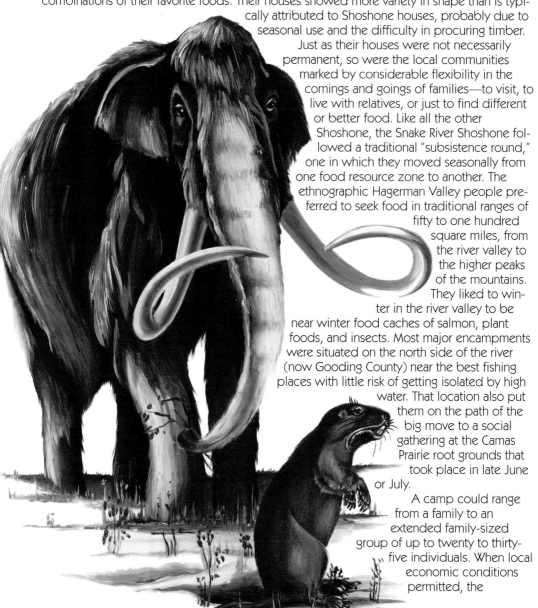

cally attributed to Shoshone houses, probably due to seasonal use and the difficulty in procuring timber. Just as their houses were not necessarily permanent, so were the local communities marked by considerable flexibility in the comings and goings of families—to visit, to live with relatives, or just to find different or better food. Like all the other Shoshone, the Snake River Shoshone followed a traditional "subsistence round," one in which they moved seasonally from one food resource zone to another. The ethnographic Hagerman Valley people preferred to seek food in traditional ranges of fifty to one hundred square miles, from the river valley to the higher peaks of the mountains. They liked to winter in the river valley to be near winter food caches of salmon, plant foods, and insects. Most major encampments were situated on the north side of the river (now Gooding County) near the best fishing places with little risk of getting isolated by high water. That location also put them on the path of the big move to a social gathering at the Camas Prairie root grounds that took place in late June or July.

A camp could range from a family to an extended family-sized group of up to twenty to thirty-five individuals. When local economic conditions permitted, the

Shoshone consolidated camps in clusters scattered from Sinking Canyon to below Bliss Hill. These so-called villages were loosely directed by a knowledgeable headman to efficiently harvest fish. This could involve harvesting at one of the early season spearfishing sites but more often involved a later season weir, dam, or basket-trap site that needed considerably lower water levels to be productive.

Making Rounds

Hagerman Valley groups did not make exclusive claims or try to defend all local resources, but neither did they accord each other free and equal use. The early spear fisheries and lower-water fisheries, which required the construction and maintenance of weirs and scaffolding, were often restricted until the occupying people had filled their winter food caches. On the other hand, the people readily shared less productive fisheries.

Despite seasonal and periodic shortages in the Hagerman area's fish runs, natives enjoyed a reasonably good life. Shoshone kin from the south came to the valley to trade, socialize, and fish. Visitors to the Upper and Lower Salmon Falls included the Humboldt Shoshone communities known as Twoqivi yuyugi (Root Jelly Eaters), Tossawi (White Knives), Wongagadu yuyugi (Pine Sitters), and Kiuyiduka (Bitterroot Eaters), all of whom traveled to the headwaters of the Bruneau and Salmon Falls Creek as part of their seasonal round. Other visitors included the Grouse Creek and Goose Creek groups known as Tukad Ka (Pine Nut Eaters) and the Tutwanait (Below or Beyond People).

During exceptional seasons, it may have been possible for a Shoshone family to survive comfortably in Hagerman Valley for nine months or more of the subsistence year. Besides salmon, other native fish should have been available to such skilled fishermen as the local Shoshone, as well as big game for protein, tools, and clothes. The people could ambush deer in the

The poisonous Death Camas could be distinguished from the edible Blue Camas only by its white flowers. Early Shoshone suffered vomiting, diarrhea, and muscle weakness if they accidentally ate its bulbs, but crushed them to poultice burns, boils, and rattlesnake bites. Left: earliest people shared the southern Idaho plain with wooly mammoths and prairie dogs.

desert to the south of the Hagerman Fossil Beds, and winter storms might have occasionally brought large herds of mountain sheep, antelope, and possibly even bison and elk down to the bluff rim. Small animals like rabbits and marmots presented trapping and encounter hunting opportunities, as did waterfowl and other game birds. Some of the hardest evidence to recover

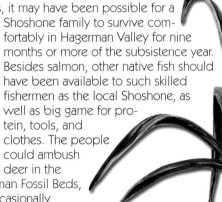

relates to the supposed gathering and collecting of seeds, roots, leaves, berries, insects, eggs, larvae, reptiles, and mussels. The "gathereds and collecteds" were often a principal focus for the Snake River Shoshone while they waited for the first anadromous fish to arrive.

The exploitation of salmon, however, is clearly fundamental to a more exact determination of the date and extent of the Shoshone ethnographic pattern. Historically, their technology included spears, harpoons, jiggling hooks, hand nets, dams, weirs, and basket traps. Such a varied technology obviously developed over time; relic collections from Upper and Lower Salmon Falls show considerable variety in fishing harpoons and fish spear tips.

The first fish available to local Shoshone were the steelhead that came in March or April. Chinook followed in May and June, with a big run usually in September and October. If the first of the runs seemed poor, groups and families might start "up-country" or move up or down the river. Most Hagerman Valley Shoshone families went away from the river valley at midsummer anyway. They returned in time for the fall fish runs, bringing with them raw material for tools and food taken from the up-country. They boiled the meat of large animals in baskets or in clay pots, and dried or broiled it in strips. They roasted smaller animals whole in fires or earth ovens and dried or pulverized them on a metate, a flat grinding stone. Small animal bones and fish bones were sometimes ground and added to soup or flour. They ate many of the fish fresh; others went into gruel, or were air dried and stored in grass-lined cache pits. They

Gooding County tablelands. Above: grasshopper, a vital protein source. Right: prehistoric house type.

ate vegetables raw, boiled, poached, or dried and sometimes ground them into flour for cakes that might also include ground bone, fish meat, reptile meat, and even insects.

With the arrival of the horse, presumably from Spanish conquistador stock between 1650 and 1700, the Shoshone bands based on the eastern fringe of the Snake River Plain expanded their settlement/subsistence possibilities to include joining their Eastern Shoshone kin in bison hunting and raiding on the northern plains. Around 1700, a group of about 600 Northern Paiute from the area of western Idaho/eastern Oregon joined the newly horsed Shoshone. Those people became known as the Bannock. In just a few years, mounted bands from the east probably visited relatives at the fisheries of Hagerman Valley. The Sho-Ban horsemen were often shadowed by their enemies, specifically the Blackfoot, who further strained the area's food animal resources and probably also captured some of the locals for slaves.

By the mid-1750s, their inability to find a good trading partner for firearms had placed the mounted Shoshone at a serious disadvantage since their enemies had amassed a great deal of firepower. Between 1750 and 1811, the mounted Shoshone came into conflict with some of the plateau groups located north and west of the Snake River Plain. Visiting equestrians probably controlled some of the peripheral salmon fisheries in this area by 1800. Also, marriage alliances and old friendships would have brought families of horsemen visiting their pedestrian friends. The Hagerman Valley fishermen continued to live without horses until the mid-1840s, quite content with their traditional lifestyle.

Grave Matters

Mining, farming, ranching, and the collecting of artifacts have destroyed many archaeological sites. Some may now be covered by the Lower Salmon Falls Reservoir. Scientists have located fewer than 25 graves in all of the Americas older than 8,500 years, most revealing only bone and artifact fragments. Buhla's recovery caused much excitement. State archaeologist Tom Green first estimated her age at 5,000 to 8,000 years. The Sho-Ban Tribal Council at Fort Hall agreed to more scientific tests.

Buhla's bone samples—part of her right humerus and a piece of rib—went to the University of California, Riverside, in 1989 but sat in limbo due to internal problems at the facility. Meanwhile, the rest of her skeleton and the artifacts were cleaned and cataloged in Boise, then sent to the Idaho State Museum of Natural History in Pocatello. The Sho-Ban requested they not be displayed there. Almost two years passed before the Idaho State Historical Society retrieved the bone samples from California and went to a commercial laboratory for carbon dating. When it finally came, the amazing date of 10,675 years plus or minus 95 made Buhla possibly the oldest skeleton on two continents. Green hoped the Sho-Ban would agree to a more thorough study, but their patience was exhausted. Elders attributed deaths on the reservation to Buhla's disturbed spirit. They wanted her reburied immediately. On an overcast December day in 1992, Green turned Buhla's skeleton and artifacts over to the Fort Hall reservation near Pocatello.

"It's a spiritual fiction to believe anyone is related to a skeleton that old," said Clement Meighan of the American Committee for the Preservation of Archaeological Collections. "Repatriation is a loaded and improper term because it implies that you're giving something back to people who own it. They don't own it and never did." But tribal attorney Janet Wolfley battled the idea that science should hold sway over native traditions. "The whole policy of digging up graves and using them finally needs to be stopped," she stated. "It's time that science gives way to people's beliefs." Jim Woods, archaeologist and director of the Herrett Museum, thought the reburial necessary—"the repayment of a long-standing political and social debt."

Wilson Butte Cave near Eden, one of North America's oldest archaeological sites. Left: woven sagebrush sandal.

Buhla offered the promise of an early window on the genetic relationships between people and the settlement of a continent. According to Clement Meighan, "Idaho really blew it." According to Nellis Burkhart, "It's kind of sacred, too, this is a human grave you're dealing with."

◆

◆ **Ronald L. James, M.A.** Hagerman Fossil Beds National Monument • **Kelly A. Murphey, M.A.** Hagerman Fossil Beds National Monument

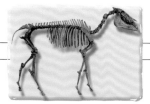
First Encounters

CHAPTER FOUR

Fur trappers and mountain men lifted the veil of mystery from the Far West in their first attempts to establish a route to the Pacific. The future Magic Valley provided a conspicuous setting for many important incidents that were part of the quest for empire in the Pacific Northwest. Euramerican impact on the Snake River Indians would forever change both cultures. The Snake near Salmon Falls supported several riverbank encampments of native people who were prominent in the early historic accounts. These people identified themselves as the Agaiduka (Salmon Eaters), Ko'a agaideka (Trap Salmon Eaters), and Pia agaideka (Big Salmon Eaters) but would become known by the names Euramericans assigned to them: Shoshone, Bannock, and Paiute.

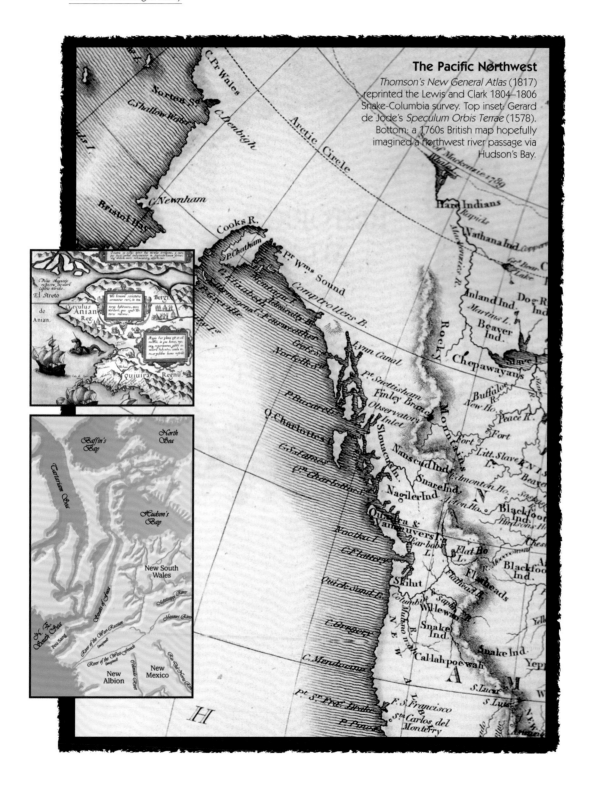

The Pacific Northwest

Thomson's New General Atlas (1817) reprinted the Lewis and Clark 1804–1806 Snake-Columbia survey. Top inset: Gerard de Jode's *Speculum Orbis Terrae* (1578). Bottom: a 1760s British map hopefully imagined a northwest river passage via Hudson's Bay.

The Snake River natives had, over millennia, developed a finely honed way of life. During the early 1800s, their way of life began undergoing unimagined transformations as Canadian and American trappers entered the Snake country. The vicinity of Upper Salmon Falls and Hagerman Valley provided the setting for some of the earliest, most vivid and detailed descriptions of Indian life on the Snake River Plain. British and American visitors recorded an invaluable and enduring legacy of ethnographic descriptions before the area was irrevocably changed.

Hunt and the Mad River

The Snake River Plain was seen as a vital trade corridor linking the Missouri with the long-sought River of the West—the mythic Northwest Passage—and the markets of China. In *Voyages through the Continent of North America* (1801), explorer Alexander Mackenzie wrote, "Whatever road one follows, on leaving the shores of the Atlantic Ocean, one must join the Columbia in order to reach the Pacific Ocean; this river is the line of communication which Nature has traced between the two seas." The Snake River Plain occupied the only feasible passageway between South Pass and the Columbia River. The Middle Snake was squarely situated on Mackenzie's "line of communication." Between 1811 and 1843, the valley was criss-crossed by many of the most celebrated trappers and mountain men of the fur trade era. Wilson Price Hunt, Donald McKenzie, John Reed, Alexander Ross, Peter Skene Ogden, Jedediah Smith, Captain Benjamin L. E. Bonneville, Kit Carson, and John Frémont all became familiar with the area's striking features such as Salmon Falls and the myriad springs and creeks.

Male freshwater-phase Snake River sockeye salmon. Previous: an Idaho Sho-Ban.

The favorable natural environment of Hagerman Valley provided a diversity of faunal and floral resources conducive to human settlement, while geographic and historical imperatives made it part of an avenue that permitted the United States continental expansion. The fur trade was everywhere in the West. It was dynamic and ruthless with cutthroat competition. Its appetite required, said historian Bernard DeVoto, "a stone age economy that meant a vast new market—beaver as common as dirt and the untouched Farther On to keep supplying it."

In 1798, Alexander Mackenzie of the Montreal-based Northwest Company became the first Euramerican to cross the North American continent north of the Rio Grande. Mackenzie failed in his efforts to trace the course of the Columbia; instead he wound up following the Peace and Bella Coola Rivers to the Pacific coast. Nevertheless, Mackenzie's epic feat of exploration gave the British a strong claim. In 1801, Mackenzie advocated a British civil and military establishment at Nootka on Vancouver Island with a "subordinate" post on the Columbia.

Mackenzie's heroic exploration and his passionate arguments failed to win appreciable support among the British leadership, which was becoming increasingly preoccupied with the Napoleonic Wars on the European continent. Mackenzie's account, however, was avidly read by Thomas Jefferson, who passed it along to Meriwether Lewis, who carried a copy to the Pacific coast during the Lewis and Clark Expedition. But it was John Jacob Astor who came the closest to actually creating the vast trade network advocated by Mackenzie. Astor had made an immense fortune in the Great Lakes fur trade dealing with the two British Canadian fur giants, the Hudson's Bay Company and the Northwest Company. Astor recognized the portentous nature of Mackenzie's exploration and realized that if he did not act immediately, the Northwest Company's drive to the Pacific could very well result in the British achieving total control of the Northwest's vast resources.

Astor's grand scheme to further expand his fur empire was comprehensive in scope and bold in design. The plan's goal was to occupy and trap the Columbia River and Rocky Mountains. The logistics were staggering, involving land and sea transportation routes in order to connect the Great Lakes with the Northwest, Russia, and China. Astor formed the Pacific

Fur Company with his own money and, with a group of Canadian and American partners, embarked on the first endeavor to establish a fur trading post at the mouth of the Columbia by sea and by land. In September 1810, Astor's ship, the *Tonquin*, sailed with men and supplies on an eventful and contentious voyage around the Horn and via Hawaii to the mouth of the Columbia, arriving in March 1811. At approximately the same time that the seaborne Astorians began to construct Fort Astoria at the Columbia's mouth, the overland expedition left St. Louis. Led by merchant Wilson Price Hunt and assisted by Donald McKenzie, Ramsay Crooks, and John Reed, the party numbering sixty-five headed for the Arikara villages on the Missouri. The overland Astorians included French Canadian voyageurs, American hunters, interpreter Pierre Dorion Jr., son of the Lewis and Clark interpreter Old Dorion, and Dorion's pregnant Iowa Indian wife and two children.

A spearfisher from Paul Kane's 1847 sketchbook. Left: Snake Indians use willow poles with detachable barbs in Bill West's study of the salmon harvest.

Originally, Hunt had planned to follow a course similar to the one taken by Lewis and Clark six years previously. He significantly altered his plan after meeting up with three veteran trappers, John Hoback, Jacob Reznor, and Edward Robinson, who had been with Andrew Henry at the forks of the Missouri the year before. The three explorers alerted Hunt to the dangers of trying to travel through the territory of the hostile Blackfoot and advised the Astorians to leave the Missouri at the Arikara villages, obtain horses, and cross the Rockies to the south toward the headwaters of the Yellowstone. In July, the Hunt party left the Arikara and the Missouri River with all their baggage packed on eighty-two horses.

Now guided by Hoback, Reznor, and Robinson, the Overland Astorians traveled westward to a tributary of the Powder River to hunt buffalo and gather an adequate supply of meat. From there they crossed through Crow tribal territory in the vicinity of Wind River, then southwest to the Green River where the Three Tetons, or Pilot Knobs, marked the headwaters of the Columbia's principal tributary, the Snake River. Here the three former Henry men suggested moving on to Henry's fort on the Snake's north branch. Hunt detached four trappers to start hunting beaver, and the Astorians, now guided by Shoshone, struggled on through the wilderness labyrinth of the Snake River's south branch, which the American trappers named Mad River. At some point during this phase of the trek, the Astorians entered present-day Idaho.

Hunt's party crossed over to the Henrys Fork of the Snake River and found the abandoned cabins and corrals built the year before by Henry's men. Here they saw a stream approximately one hundred yards wide with a strong, westward current. Not realizing it was a branch of the unnavigable river just recently labeled "mad," they decided to "pursue our journey by water." Hunt, believing he had found a safe and practical access to the Columbia, had the voyageurs start felling cottonwoods for canoes, while another detachment of trappers, including Hoback, Reznor, Robinson, and Martin Cass, was sent off into the wilderness to trap.

A Collision Course with Suffering & Death

On the 19th of October, Hunt left the horses with two Shoshone Indians that had recently attached themselves to the expedition. The Overland Astorians, now numbering fifty-five and consisting primarily of the French Canadian voyageurs including Madame Dorion and her two children, climbed into fifteen canoes and pushed off into the Snake River's current. All of the party's hopes were staked on the conjecture that the broad and placid waters of the Snake River would take them to Fort Astoria at the mouth of the Columbia. It was a decision, commented James P. Ronda, that "put the Astorians on a collision course with suffering and death."

Hunt's canoe-borne party made fast and steady progress during the first days on the river, but as they progressed down the Snake, the river began to alternate between a smooth, fast "highway to the Columbia" and a treacherous, terrifying course that courted disaster. Near the mouth of Raft River, the Astorians saw Indians fishing along the riverbank. When Hunt went ashore and attempted to meet with them, the terrified Shoshone fled at the sight of the strangers. Hunt was able to trade knives for fish with one Shoshone, but "his fear was so great that I could not persuade him to indicate by signs the route I ought to take."

Unaware of the rapids and canyons still ahead of them, the Astorians proceeded downriver in their cottonwood canoes. Disaster struck with sudden fury when, as Hunt tersely described, "On the 28th [October], our journey was less fortunate. After passing several rapids, we came to the entrance of a canyon. Mr. Crooks's canoe was upset, one of his men drowned, many goods were lost." Near the present location of Milner Dam,

Beaver and 1830s wrought-iron trap.

where the Snake begins its tumultuous descent into a spectacular canyon, the canoe carrying Ramsay Crooks struck a boulder, smashing it and drowning Antoine Clappine, who was one of the expedition's most experienced voyageurs. Hunt and his party found themselves stranded in a basaltic canyon along a terrifying stretch of the Snake River that the awestruck Scottish Astorians gave the Celtic appellation "Caldron Linn." Lost and bewildered, Hunt and clerk John Reed spent the next several days desperately scouting the Snake River Canyon, only to find that the unmerciful river continued its course through a deep canyon that prohibited further travel by canoe.

By now it was November and they had only enough food for five days. As Washington Irving described the ordeal, "To linger in the vague hope of relief ... would be to run the risk of perishing with hunger. Besides, the winter was rapidly advancing, and they had a long journey to make through an unknown country ... they were yet, in fact, a thousand miles from

Astoria, but fore and around them was vague and conjectural, and wore an aspect calculated to inspire despondency." Hunt decided the party must break up into smaller groups and

try to walk out, staking their hopes on finding Indians willing to trade for food and horses. On November 9, after caching their supply of trade goods, the Astorians broke up into three groups and set out for Astoria: Donald McKenzie marched north with four men; Hunt led twenty-two, including the Dorion family, along the north bank of the Snake; Ramsay Crooks took a group of twenty along the south bank.

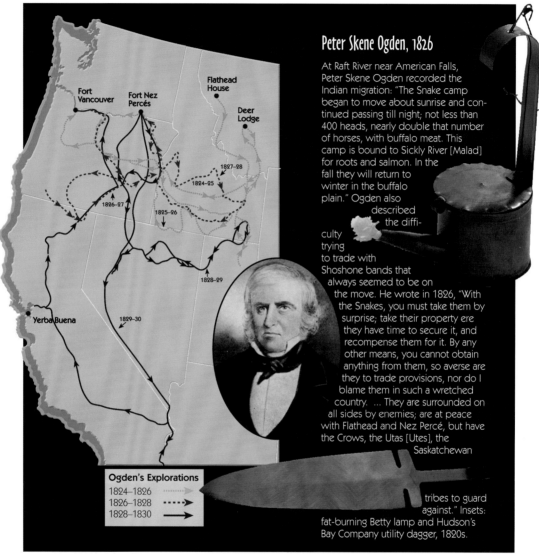

Peter Skene Ogden, 1826

At Raft River near American Falls, Peter Skene Ogden recorded the Indian migration: "The Snake camp began to move about sunrise and continued passing till night; not less than 400 heads, nearly double that number of horses, with buffalo meat. This camp is bound to Sickly River [Malad] for roots and salmon. In the fall they will return to winter in the buffalo plain." Ogden also described the difficulty trying to trade with Shoshone bands that always seemed to be on the move. He wrote in 1826, "With the Snakes, you must take them by surprise; take their property ere they have time to secure it, and recompense them for it. By any other means, you cannot obtain anything from them, so averse are they to trade provisions, nor do I blame them in such a wretched country. ... They are surrounded on all sides by enemies; are at peace with Flathead and Nez Percé, but have the Crows, the Utas [Utes], the Saskatchewan tribes to guard against." Insets: fat-burning Betty lamp and Hudson's Bay Company utility dagger, 1820s.

Ogden's Explorations
1824–1826 ·········▷
1826–1828 - - - -▶
1828–1830 ———▶

The next day, while Crooks's party likely traversed the Hagerman Fossil Beds as they followed the south bank of the Snake, Hunt's party on the north bank found a trail leading down to the river where they met two Shoshone. These were the first Indians Hunt had encountered since Raft River. One of the Shoshone had a knife he had received from another of the Astorian parties. Hunt wrote, "One of them led us by a path that took us away from the river. We crossed a prairie, and arrived at a camp of his tribe," probably in the vicinity of present-day Hagerman. The camp Hunt visited was fairly populous for a winter encampment, with a

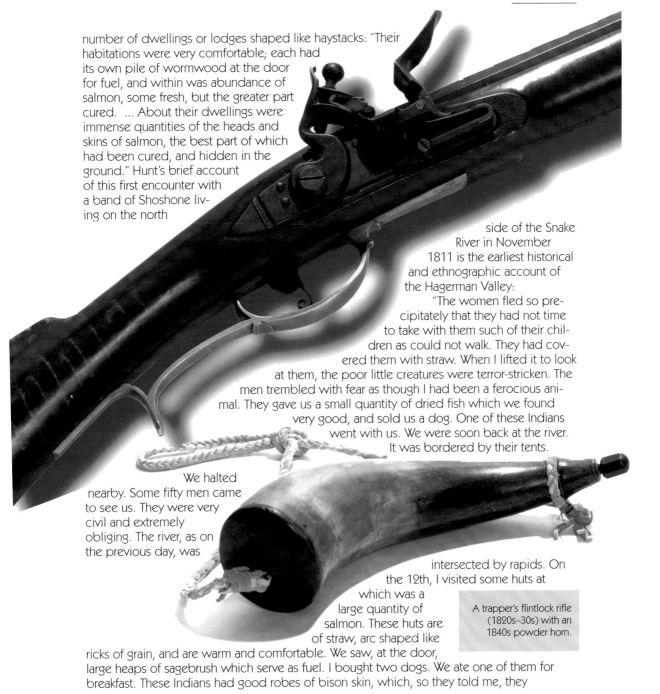

number of dwellings or lodges shaped like haystacks: "Their habitations were very comfortable; each had its own pile of wormwood at the door for fuel, and within was abundance of salmon, some fresh, but the greater part cured. ... About their dwellings were immense quantities of the heads and skins of salmon, the best part of which had been cured, and hidden in the ground." Hunt's brief account of this first encounter with a band of Shoshone living on the north side of the Snake River in November 1811 is the earliest historical and ethnographic account of the Hagerman Valley:

"The women fled so precipitately that they had not time to take with them such of their children as could not walk. They had covered them with straw. When I lifted it to look at them, the poor little creatures were terror-stricken. The men trembled with fear as though I had been a ferocious animal. They gave us a small quantity of dried fish which we found very good, and sold us a dog. One of these Indians went with us. We were soon back at the river. It was bordered by their tents.

We halted nearby. Some fifty men came to see us. They were very civil and extremely obliging. The river, as on the previous day, was intersected by rapids. On the 12th, I visited some huts at which was a large quantity of salmon. These huts are of straw, arc shaped like

A trapper's flintlock rifle (1820s–30s) with an 1840s powder horn.

ricks of grain, and are warm and comfortable. We saw, at the door, large heaps of sagebrush which serve as fuel. I bought two dogs. We ate one of them for breakfast. These Indians had good robes of bison skin, which, so they told me, they obtained in exchange for their salmon. On leaving them, we marched some distance from the river and crossed a small stream [the Malad River]. We saw mountains to the north."

Just as Nez Percé generosity helped preserve the Lewis and Clark Expedition on the Wieppe Prairie in 1805, the Shoshone camped in the Hagerman Valley provided Hunt's Overland Astorians with food and provisions in a country that was destitute of game. Some of the Shoshone bands on the north side of the Snake River were apparently more prosperous than the bands living on the southern bank. Downriver from Salmon Falls, in the vicinity of King Hill, Hunt observed that most of the Shoshone had garments made from buffalo and reported seeing some horses that were a form of wealth that had to be vigilantly protected from roving war parties. Hunt had no opportunity to trade for horses because their protective and wary owners "took great pains to keep them out of our way."

Hunt had more success getting food on the Snake's north bank than Crooks had on the river's south side. When Hunt and Crooks met up near the present location of Homestead, Oregon, Crooks and his twenty companions were on the verge of starvation, having subsisted for the last nine days on "one beaver, a dog, a few wild cherries, and some old mockason sole." Before the ordeal was over, the Snake claimed another of the Canadian voyageurs, and Madame Dorion gave birth to a baby that died a few days later. Hunt's party arrived at Astoria on February 15, 1812. The emaciated Crooks party appeared several weeks later.

Scottish-born Robert Stuart, who had gone to Astoria by sea on the *Tonquin*, made an even more significant contribution than Hunt to exploring what would become the Oregon Trail. In June 1812, Stuart and five fellow Astorians left Fort Astoria and embarked on an eastward trek to carry dispatches back to Astor in New York. Stuart kept a journal documenting the overland journey of what Alexander Ross called "this little, bold, and courageous party."

Mule deer at the base of the Sawtooths. So plentiful were deer in the Snake River country that hunters later sold venison by the wagonload to miners and railroad workers for about three cents a pound.

From Astoria to the Snake River, Stuart traveled the same route in reverse that Hunt had used. He and his party passed through the vicinity of the Hagerman Valley and Lower Salmon Falls during the last days of August, a time of year Stuart described as "the prime of the fishing season in this Country." These midsummer salmon runs were capable of temporarily supporting fairly large tribal gatherings in the Hagerman Valley, and the Astorians had the incredible opportunity to witness the Shoshone harvesting salmon. Stuart reported "about one hundred lodges of Shoshonies busily occupied in Killing & drying Fish" near Lower Salmon Falls. "The Fish begin to jump soon after sunrise," Stuart continued. "Indians in great numbers with their spears swim in, to near the centre of the Falls, where some

placing themselves on Rocks & others to their middle in Water, darts on all sides assail the Salmon, who struggling to ascend, and perhaps exhausted with repeated efforts, become an

Pierre. — Rocky m....t

easy prey. With the greatest facility prodigious quantities are slaughtered daily and it must have been from this place that the dead & wounded came which we saw picked up by the starving wretches below; am completely at a loss to conceive why these [poor] creatures do not prefer mingling with their own nation at this immense fishing place (where a few hours exertion would produce more than a months labour in their own way); rather than depend on the uncertainty of a Fish ascending close along shore or catching a part of what few make their escape wounded From these Falls."

Massacred & Blown Up

Stuart and his men traded with the Indians at Lower Salmon Falls and then recommenced their journey up the river and onto the hilly uplands overlooking the Upper Salmon Falls and possibly the fossil beds. From this vantage, Stuart could see the Upper Salmon Falls, which he described as "considerable rapids." As they left the vicinity of Salmon Falls Creek bound upstream for Hunt's caches, Stuart was joined by "two Indians their Squaws & one child" who had five horses. These five

Indians were also headed eastward and wanted to accompany Stuart's party, perhaps seeking protection from any Blackfoot war parties that might attempt to steal their horses. Four

days later, Stuart and his party were at Caldron Linn and located the nine caches that Hunt had left; six of the caches had been opened, but the three remaining caches still contained dry goods, ammunition, and traps, all of which the Astorians took.

The remainder of Stuart's crossing was fraught with peril and difficulty; the

The inaccessible Snake River below Twin Falls. For twenty-eight miles in November 1811 these perpendicular precipices of solid rock barred the Wilson Price Hunt party from replenishing its water supply. Washington Irving reported that trappers recycled their urine: "The thirst of some of the Canadian voyagers became so insupportable as to drive them to most revolting means." Left: Alfred Jacob Miller's *Pierre—a Rocky Mountain Trapper*, about 1837.

Crow stole their horses, and they almost starved to death near Jackson Hole. But on the way out of Jackson Hole, they chose to follow an Indian trail west of the mountains instead of following Hunt's trail north. This route led to Stuart's accidental discovery of South Pass on October 23, 1812. The consequences of Stuart's discovery would be momentous. South Pass was the ideal passageway for wagons to cross through the Rocky Mountains and would become "the hub of transportation in the Far West." Stuart's discovery of South Pass was kept a company secret for years afterward by Astor. Jedediah Smith's 1824 rediscovery of the gap, offering an easy crossing of the Rockies, made the public first aware of "a passage by which loaded waggons can ... reach the navigable waters of the Columbia River."

What the Astorians saw of Indian life was a less than pristine aboriginal culture. By the early 1750s, Blackfoot firepower had pushed as many as 3,000 to 4,000 equestrian Northern Shoshone and Bannock back onto the Snake River Plain. Many of these mounted Indians visited the fisheries of the Middle Snake and in the process brought their enemies with them as well. The few horses seen by Hunt and Stuart may have belonged to Shoshone or Bannock visiting local Shoshone who were relatives, or the animals may have been gifts.

Fort Astoria on the Columbia was meanwhile dogged by a series of disasters. After depositing men and supplies at the mouth of the Columbia, Astor's ship, the *Tonquin*, sailed north to Vancouver Island to trade with the coastal tribes. While anchored off the island, the entire crew was massacred and the ship blown up. A few months later, war broke out between Britain and the United States. Fearing a British naval assault, Astor's partners sold Astoria to the British Canadian Northwest Company. Since many of the Astorians were Scottish or Canadian, most simply switched sides and went back to work as "Nor'westers." The new owners of the post changed the name to Fort George and assumed what amounted to virtual British control of the Northwest, but the founding of Astoria as an American outpost would continue to provide the United States with a strong claim to the Oregon Country.

A Shoshone doll. Right: Pocatello's warriors wear trade beads and machine-made blankets in this photograph from the 1870s.

The Northwest Company launched the first of a series of Snake Brigades that systematically began trapping the tributaries of the Snake River. For a time between the years 1815 and 1821, Nor'westers pushed deep into the Snake River Plain and beyond to the Rocky Mountains, dominating all the land west of the Rockies and north of the Great Salt Lake. Donald McKenzie, the massive 300-pound former Astorian whom Alexander Ross called "Perpetual Motion," led the first expedition into the Snake Country in 1818 for the Northwest Company. The first Snake Expedition consisted of fifty-five Iroquois, Abenaki, Hawaiians, and French Canadians, equipped with 195 horses and 300 beaver traps. For the better part of three years, McKenzie sent trapping parties throughout the country between the Snake and Green Rivers. Mckenzie passed through the Hagerman Valley in 1818 and may have trapped in the vicinity during 1819. The killing of three of McKenzie's Hawaiian trappers in what is now southwest Idaho gave the river there the name Owyhee, which was then the spelling for Hawaii. His most notable accomplishment was revolutionizing the Northwest fur trade, and he certainly ranks as one of the period's most important explorers.

By the time McKenzie arrived in southern Idaho in 1818, the Indians on the Snake River Plain were experiencing serious threats to traditional food resources while simultaneously finding themselves living in a combination war zone and trade thoroughfare. McKenzie was forced to broker a peace agreement between various factions of Shoshone, Bannock, and Nez Percé before he could set his traps in the Snake country. Meanwhile, Blackfoot war

parties roamed southcentral Idaho at will. From these early encounters, Native Americans and trappers became intertwined in a complex pattern of exchange. From the Indians, the fur

trappers received guidance, food, and horses. Access to the white man's manufactured goods had a staggering impact on Indians. Trade goods such as metal awls, fishhooks, knives, cloth, beads, bells, buttons, and brass rings were very much in demand, and Indians also avidly sought firearms and tobacco. It is not known to what extent such trading proved genuinely advantageous for the Salmon Falls Shoshone. The trade goods came with a steep price: increased exposure to predatory foes, loss of food resources, and disruption of the traditional seasonal rounds.

The More We Impoverish the Country

The Snake Brigades made the Hagerman Valley a focal point for the dramatic cultural changes and the diffusion of cultural traits and materials that irrevocably altered the Indian way of life. Several examples of trade goods were among the items loot- ed by relic diggers from burial sites located near the east side of Lower Salmon Falls. Many of those burials may have been the result of epidemics from diseases introduced by Euramericans. The white man's diseases had preceded even Lewis and Clark by a hundred years. Measles, whooping cough, smallpox, tuberculosis, and diphtheria had rav- aged Missouri River village tribes, and epidemics also swept through the Spanish settlements in California and the Russian outposts in Alaska. Former Idaho state archaeologist Tom Green has estimated that half of North America's indigenous people died of European diseases before any Europeans saw them. Indian populations living in constant and close contact with one another, such as the communal fishing camps in the Hagerman Valley, would have been especially vulnerable to the exotic diseases introduced by the early fur trappers.

Between 1818 and 1845, the United States and Great Britain made several unsuccessful attempts to negotiate a partition of the Oregon Country. In 1821, the Northwest Company and the even more powerful Hudson's Bay Company merged in order to end a trade war. The newly combined fur trade conglomerate kept the name and charter of the Hudson's Bay Company and received from the British government a monopoly over all British trade in the Oregon Country. In 1824, HBC reorgan- ized its Columbia department. The company moved its

Brass powder horn and Shoshone war club, about 1850. Left: bobcat captures muskrat.

headquarters from Fort George, formerly Astoria, inland to a more strategic location on the north side of Columbia near the confluence of the Willamette. The new base was named Fort Vancouver, and its new chief factor was Dr. John McLoughlin, a man who would dominate the affairs of the Oregon Country for the next two decades.

The Hudson's Bay Company also changed the way the Snake Country Expeditions were conducted. HBC governor George Simpson ordered the Snake Country stripped of beaver. "The more we impoverish the country" reasoned Simpson, "the less likelihood is there of our being assailed by opposition." Between 1822 and 1824, three HBC brigades were sent into the Snake Country from Flathead Post in what is now northeast Montana. Michel Bourdon led the 1822 expedition, and Finian McDonald led the 1823 Snake Brigade. Former Astorian and Nor'wester Alexander Ross was given command of the third Snake Brigade.

Ross's contribution to the early history of southern Idaho and the Snake River country was impressive. In 1824, Ross named the Malad River at the northern end of Hagerman Valley after most of his fur brigade took ill while camped along the stream from eating beaver that had eaten hemlock. He was the first Euramerican to cross the divide between the sources of the Big Wood and Salmon Rivers and the first to explore Wood River Valley. In 1824, Ross also recorded an observation concerning the impact of the fur trade and the horse culture on the region's tribes. While in the vicinity of the Camas Prairie, a Shoshone (or possibly a Bannock) told him, "We can never venture in the open plains for fear of the Blackfoot and Piegans, and for that reason never keep horses. Six of our people were killed last summer. Were we to live in large bands, we should easily be discovered."

At this time William H. Ashley's men began canvassing the Far West. These were the free American trappers who would become the legendary "mountain men." One of Ashley's men, Jedediah Smith, met up with Ross's Snake Brigade in October 1824 and followed him back to the Flathead Post. In essence, Ross inadvertently provided Smith with a guided tour of the HBC's Rocky Mountain domain. Ross

Science moved west with a London-made sextant of the type topographers used on the Pacific Railroad Surveys. Left: brass sundial timepiece, about 1810. Right: an angel strings telegraph wire in this detail from John Gast's 1872 *American Progress.* Below: the electric telegraph, invented in 1832, reached Salt Lake City in 1861, Shoshone and Hailey in 1883.

was replaced by the ruthless Peter Skene Ogden, who led the Snake Brigades for the next six years.

Smith's incursion into the British-dominated Snake Country marked the beginning of a relentless American campaign that would eventually drive the British from the Snake and Columbia Rivers. While exploring the northern Great Basin for the mythical Buenaventura River during the spring of 1826, Smith crossed the barren Salt Flats of Utah, entering what is now eastern Nevada, but near starvation drove him to follow Salmon Falls Creek north to the Snake River. After crossing the Snake below the Lower Salmon Falls, Smith headed north to the Boise River. He continued on to the Payette before retracing his route back to the Boise, east to the Big Wood, then to the Big Lost River, and on toward the Cache Valley.

Peter Skene Ogden, Smith's rival, hated the Snake Country. "A more gloomy country I never yet saw" is how he once described it in his journal. For six long years, Ogden led the Hudson's Bay Company Snake Brigade with courage and skill. No other trapper, mountain man, or explorer saw as much of the Oregon Country and the Great Basin as he did. During his years in the Snake Country, Ogden passed through the Hagerman Valley on at least two occasions. Like Stuart and Ross, he was an astute and keen observer; the journal recording his second expedition is one of the great accounts of western exploration (the journal from Ogden's first Snake expedition is another of the West's great missing documents).

The American trappers were more opportunistic than the British, constantly searching for more economic possibilities than hunting beaver. New England ice merchant Nathaniel Wyeth attempted a mercantile scheme on a scale as grand as Astor's. In 1832, Wyeth visited a Shoshone encampment near Salmon Falls. "From these Indians," he wrote on August 30, "I procured fresh salmon spawn which was very encouraging as we are nearly out of provisions and the country would afford us scanty subsistence."

Wyeth returned to the West in 1834 with supplies and merchandise for the annual Rocky Mountain Fur Company rendezvous. But competitor William Sublette reached the rendezvous site first, and the late-arriving Wyeth was able to dispose of only a small portion of his merchandise. He moved on westward to the valley of the Snake and located a site to build a trading post near the mouth of the Portneuf. On August 4, Wyeth completed construction of Fort Hall. In a countermove, Hudson's Bay built a rival trading post, Fort Boise, on the mouth of the Boise River. Both forts became famous and important trading posts on the emigrant trails. In 1837, Wyeth sold Fort Hall to the Hudson's Bay Company. Even though Wyeth's Oregon venture ended in failure, he significantly influenced the direction of the American westward movement. In historian Hubert Howe Bancroft's assessment, "It was [Wyeth] who, more directly than any other man, marked the way for the ox-teams which were so shortly to bring the Americanized civilization ... across the roadless continent."

Fracture & Violence & Fire

Captain Bonneville and Lt. John Charles Frémont, two of the West's most notable military engineers, were agents of continental expansion. Bonneville spent 1831 to 1835 in the West on a leave of absence from the U.S. Army, ostensibly as a private fur trapper but in actuality a semiofficial spy. He traversed the central and northern Rockies and the Oregon Country, all the while ascertaining the courses of principal rivers, the location of Indian tribes, the disposition of

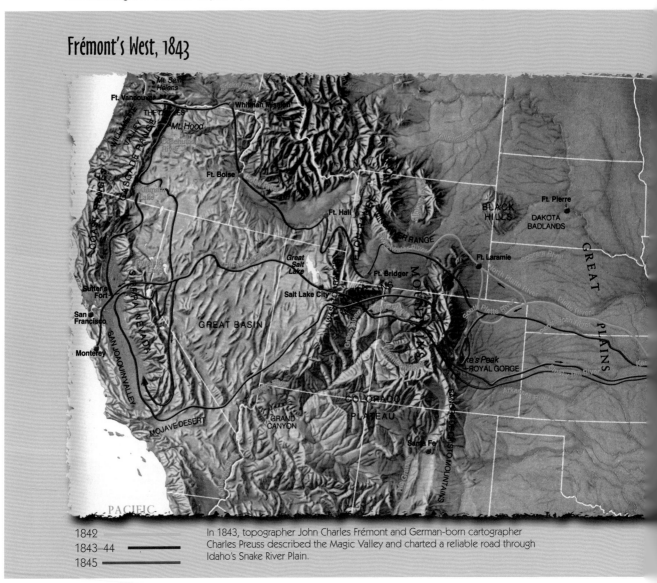

Frémont's West, 1843

1842
1843–44 ━━━━
1845 ━━━━━━

In 1843, topographer John Charles Frémont and German-born cartographer Charles Preuss described the Magic Valley and charted a reliable road through Idaho's Snake River Plain.

Hudson's Bay Company operations in Oregon, and the activities of Mexicans south of the 42nd parallel. Bonneville's journal has since been lost, but Washington Irving used Bonneville's account as the basis for his 1837 book, *The Adventures of Captain Bonneville*.

"[Their] dress," wrote Irving of the Shoshone, "consisted of a mantle about four feet square, formed of strips of rabbit skin sewed together; this they hung over their shoulders, in the ordinary Indian mode of wearing the blanket. Their weapons were bows and arrows; the latter tipped with obsidian, which abounds in the neighborhood. Their huts were shaped like haystacks, and con-structed of branches of willow covered with long grass, so as to be warm and comfortable. Occasionally, they were surrounded by small inclosures of wormwood, about three feet high, which gave them a cottage-like appearance. Three or four of these tenements were occasionally grouped together in some wild and striking situation ... sometimes they were in sufficient number to form a small hamlet. From the people, Captain Bonneville's party frequently purchased salmon. This seemed to be their prime article of food; but they were extremely anxious to get buffalo meat in exchange."

Like Bonneville, John C. Frémont was an army officer sent west who had his subsequent adventures well publicized. Frémont became one of the preeminent explorers of the American West in the nineteenth century, leading five expeditions between 1842 and 1853. Known as "the Pathfinder," Frémont was actually "the Great Publicist" who lured settlers west with his vivid reports, maps, and narratives of the routes to Oregon and California. On his second expedition, in 1843, Frémont reconnoitered South Pass and explored the Great Salt Lake. He then traversed the Oregon Trail to Fort Vancouver, ventured into southeast Oregon and northwest Nevada, crossed the Sierra Nevada range and wintered with John Sutter, toured various California towns, and returned to the Rockies by a southerly route.

American eagle clutches arrows and a peace pipe on John C. Frémont's home-made flag, 1842. Below: topographer Frémont.

Frémont's contingent of thirty-nine men was mostly French Canadian, but the party also included cartographer Charles Preuss and mountain men Kit Carson, Thomas "Broken Hand" Fitzpatrick, and Alexis Godey. Preuss served as the expedition's scientist; he mapped the topography of the entire route, collected plant and mineral specimens, and sketched scenes depicting the landscapes, including one of Thousand Springs entitled "Outlet of Subterranean River." Frémont's report included a vivid description of Salmon Falls, while Section VI of Preuss's topographical map clearly delineates the location of Fishing Falls 1,300 miles from Westport Landing. The Shoshone were quite numerous, "strung along the river at every little rapid where fish are to be caught, and the cry haggai, haggai (fish), was constantly heard whenever we passed near their huts, or met them in the road."

Cartographer Preuss kept a diary that was discovered in 1954. While Frémont was often grandiose and theatrical, Preuss was grouchy and terse. When Frémont brought along a twelve-pound brass cannon for no other reason than its symbolic value, Preuss complained, "If we had only left that ridiculous thing at home." For Preuss, the Snake River Plain was "terrible," the weather cold and windy, "the road rocky." Preuss, however, was impressed by the Hagerman

Frémont's scout Sergeant Jim, about 1843. Below: fur-era musket balls and pouch. Right: Bill West's depiction of salmon.

Valley. "Yesterday we passed the Fishing Falls. Now we can purchase salmon to our heart's content. ... One hears nothing but the word haggai, fish. ... This Snake River is interesting, I must confess, no matter how awful the country around it may be. The most beautiful little waterfalls, twenty to forty feet high."

In 1845 the publication of Frémont's report began an era that would culminate in the fulfillment of America's manifest destiny. Oregon overlanders relied extensively on assistance and trade from the Shoshone at Salmon Falls, just as Hunt's 1811 Overland Astorians, Wyeth in 1832, and Frémont had done. Historian Elliot West's description of the frontier as "a place of accommodation and exchange," a shifting and unstable "zone of exchange and mutual influence," was certainly applicable to the future Magic Valley during the early fur trade era. Zones of exchange such as the Middle Snake were critical during the early years of contact, for within these designated areas Euramericans and Native Americans depended upon each other for articles of trade, lived together, learned to speak to each other, ate each other's cooking, and engaged in mercantile exchanges. But in the end, the Native American people lost their autonomy as their subsistence-based culture was undercut by the overwhelming currents of Euramerican westward migration and a growing market economy.

◆

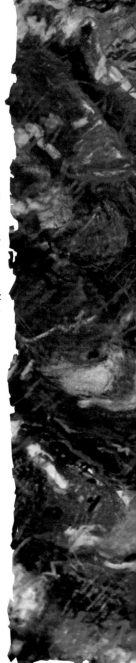

Todd Shallat, Ph.D.
History, Boise State University
Ambrose Richardson
History, Boise State University

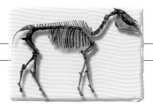

The Devil's Backbone

CHAPTER FIVE

bove rapids thick with salmon at mile 1,367 of the 2,170-mile journey from Independence, Missouri, to Oregon City, Oregon, the trail humped over a bluff. Oxen struggled in the sandy soil of fossil-rich flood deposits. Jesse A. Applegate walked. "In getting away from this place we had a narrow escape," wrote Applegate in *Recollections of My Boyhood*. Age six in 1843, he tugged at his mother's side in a train of 875 pioneers and twice that number of livestock—the largest caravan yet to follow the Oregon Trail. Dark cliffs above the Snake River at Salmon Falls startled the Missouri farm boy. "We had to follow the Devil's Backbone," Applegate recollected. "It is a very narrow ridge with a gorge a thousand feet deep on the left hand and a sheer precipice on the right." No child who could toddle or walk was allowed to cross in a wagon. Between iron-hooped wheels and certain disaster were barely inches to spare.

"Strait is the gate and narrow is the way which leadeth unto life," wrote Applegate in 1914, near death and quoting from Scripture. "Wide is the gate and broad is the way that leadeth to destruction. But this Devil's Backbone was worse than either, for it was both narrow and crooked, and it was hard to tell where it might lead to."

Narrow and steep, the well-rutted Devil's Backbone led to a West of graver hazards.
Right: W. H. D. Koerner's *Madonna of the Prairie* (1922) depicts Molly Wingate, heroine of Emerson Hough's *The Covered Wagon.* On April 1, 1922, *Madonna* graced the cover of *The Saturday Evening Post.* The novel inspired the Paramount motion picture that became Hollywood's first western epic. The 1930 sequel premiered in Idaho at Boise's Egyptian Theater during the Oregon Trail centennial.

Often the road beyond Hagerman led to a West of graver hazards; it led, in Applegate's recollections, to a swollen ford of the Snake at Three Islands, a scaffoldlike tomb of hanging corpses near Fort Boise, a near-fatal fall under a wagon wheel in Oregon's Malheur Desert, a rock-and-spear-throwing brawl with Indian youths outside Fort Walla Walla, an early snowfall in the Blue Mountains, and then calamity at The Dalles of the Columbia where a skiff disappeared in a whirlpool, killing three. Shrouded in lore and idealization, the trail led also to myth. Oregon in the 1840s was national wish fulfillment. God's Country. A window on the Pacific. A pastoral Eden beyond the Indian country where righteous yeomen staked claim to the fertile Northwest. "Oregon," said the *Alton Telegraph,* "would contribute to our national honor." It would "connect the North with the South, and the East with the West, so firmly that nothing but the power of Omnipotence could separate them or prevent the United States from becoming the leading nation of the world." First, however, Americans would have to drive "an entering wedge" through the Snake River's lava landscape. Why go to Oregon? asked John Quincy Adams. "To make the wilderness blossom as the rose, to establish laws, to increase, multiply, and subdue the earth which we are commanded to do by the first behest of God Almighty."

The imagery demonized Idaho. Where the August heat left little forage for livestock and the buffalo had been hunted to near extinction, the Snake cut vertical chasms through a waste of ghoulish place-names: *Gate of Death* (renamed Massacre Rocks), *Caldron Linn* (the river's "boiling, seething cauldron" that killed a trapper in 1811), *Devil's Scuttle Hole* (the 35 miles of rapids above Twin Falls), *Rattlesnake Creek* (near Mountain Home), *Malad Gorge* (north of Hagerman where the French-named *Riviere Malades,* or "sick river," entered the Snake). The not-yet Magic Valley seemed sinister, even satanic. "How old man Vulcan has played Havoc here," said mapmaker Charles Preuss.

Never mind that the ghouls were mostly imagined. And never mind that the drop from Hagerman's hump—about 400 feet—was less than half what a farm boy recollected. Fear was a rite of passage on Idaho's road to Canaan. Pioneer Elizabeth Miller Applegate, Jesse's mother, hid a pistol in her apron. Her terror of the desert was genuine whether the dangers were real or not.

Children of Israel

And yet they came, streaming toward Oregon sunsets. By 1846, at least 5,000 settlers had reached Oregon's Willamette Valley via the Snake-Columbia basin. Others abandoned the Snake at Raft River (one hundred miles or so before reaching the Devil's Backbone) where the trail branched south toward the promise of California.

Estimates vary. Historian Aubrey Haines of the National Park Service counted 43,264 Oregon-bound emigrants for the years 1841–1863. Historian John D. Unruh Jr., greatly enlarged the estimate by factoring in the many thousands who arrived via detours and cutoffs. From 1840 to 1860, according to Unruh's calculations, 253,397 reached the Shoshone country via South Pass and Fort Hall. Billowing west in one of history's most impulsive migrations, an estimated 300,000 reached the Pacific by wagon before cannons bombarded Fort Sumter. Murder, massacre, and massive flooding in the early 1860s only suspended the wagon migration. Even after 1869, when a golden spike at Promontory Point, Utah, completed a rail connection between California and Missouri, the old Snake-Columbia road freighted most of the Oregon traffic. Not until the Oregon Short Line's 1884 bridge over the Snake above Huntington did rails supercede trails.

America's destiny was manifest in those hordes hurtling westward. So said Francis Parkman, the wealthy adventurer who, in 1846, traveled as far as Nebraska and published a popular book that gave the migration its name. "The Indians will soon be abased by whiskey and overawed by military posts," wrote Parkman in *The Oregon Trail*. Wild and noble and caught in the great invasion like the buffalo on which they depended, the natives seemed dumbfounded and doomed. The Oglala, for example, "were [not] in the slightest degree modified by their contact with civilization. They know nothing of the power and real character of the white men, and their children would scream in terror when they saw me." White men knew even less of the red. Gawking emigrants were "tall, awkward men in brown home-spun [and] women with cadaverous faces." Children lost in the woods, they were "totally out of their element, bewildered and amazed."

The Oregon Trail spawned a folk genre of memoirs and guide-books, of Currier & Ives prints and barroom murals, of prairie schooners breasting amber grasslands. Not until Frederick Jackson Turner, however, did the trail swell to mythic importance as a highway of national identity. "The frontier," wrote Turner in an 1893 address to the American Historical Association, "was the most rapid and effective line of Americanization." The Old West had "consolidated" national culture with enduring characteristics, namely "that practical, inventive turn of mind, quick to find expedients; that masterful grasp of material things, lacking in the artistic but powerful to effect great ends; that restless, nervous energy; that dominant individual-ism, working for good and for evil, and withal that buoy-ancy and exuberance which comes with freedom." The Oregon Trail—for Turner an idea more than a highway—was a vital stage of a sweeping process that year after year had replenished America's virtue and strength.

Warfare and reservations had pacified the Oregon Trail by the time President Benjamin Harrison, who signed Idaho into statehood, issued this commemorative medal as a peace offering to the displaced western tribes. Left: U.S. Army service medal, 1880s.

Historians ever since have searched for America's cen-ter on the frontier's moving edge. Taking a cue from Turner, who compared "the progress from savage conditions" to Darwin's theory of evolution, the World War I-era historian T. C. Elliott claimed that the Americans who settled Oregon were simply "the fittest to survive." Likewise in 1929 the his-torian Agnes Laut called the emigrants "Children of Israel," their trail a "racial highway." Superior breeding, again, was the engine of civilization in the Federal Writers' Project 1939 Oregon Trail guide: "The biological genes transmitting the characteristics that drained Europe of much of its vitality and made the United States an empire extending from coast to coast have not been bred out." Territorial conquest, a biological imperative, was inevitable and therefore right.

As history became metaphysics, the emigrant corridor all but vanished as a physical space. In 1914, after a search of the Idaho Statehouse, a historical society founder wrote a letter to a patron in Caldwell. "I regret," said John Hailey, "that I have no map of the Old Oregon road." Nor had he ever seen one. The desert passage, he continued, had never been a single road: it was a swath of parallel trails a mile across in places. Ironically it was Hailey, formerly a stagecoach entrepreneur, who had done as much as any one man to scatter the original trail. Eighty-five percent of the nineteenth-century road had been plowed or paved or otherwise obliterated by the time Congress, in 1978, granted historic landmark status to what shrinking mileage remained. The trail, said a 1999 report to the National Park Service, was "a symbol of westward expansion [that embodied] traditional concepts of pioneer spir-it, patriotism, and rugged individualism." But which set of ruts best embodied that

Americanism? Decades of meticulous work by a dozen or more state and federal agencies have since rediscovered and mapped 318 miles, mostly in Wyoming. Three difficult miles (and perhaps another three waiting for further study) dissect the Hagerman Fossil Beds National Monument.

"It is rare to see history pure and undisturbed," said Idaho's department of tourism in its brochure on the Oregon Trail. Rare—but not in Idaho where "the landscape is exactly as the emigrants left it," where the tourist willing to step away from the highway can "almost imperceptibly hear the creak of the axles, the lowing of the oxen, the crying of babies." Atop the Devil's Backbone that tourist could almost hear and see what Applegate recollected if not for back-flooded rapids, row crops, barbed wire, cattle crossings, and a slashing line of steel towers that harnesses the Hagerman Valley to a power grid larger than France.

Thomas Moran's *Shoshone Falls on Snake River*. Painted in 1900, Moran's eleven-foot canvas celebrated the Magic Valley landmark as a symbol of wild nature and the epitome of the sublime.

It is rare to see history pure—especially rare in a flood-swept lava desert where ordinary farmers in an extraordinary migration transformed a remarkable land.

Oregon or the Grave

Across the wide Missouri and up the Platte to the Colorado Rockies, then south to the Texas Panhandle through trials of heat, thirst, desertion, theft, near mutiny, and near starvation, Maj. Stephen Long, in 1820, led the scientific wing of the army's Yellowstone expedition to the psychological edge of American civilization. "In regards to this section of country," wrote Long, an engineer from rainy New England, "we do not hesitate in giving the opinion that it is almost wholly unfit for cultivation, and of course uninhabitable by a people depending upon agriculture for their subsistence." Printed across Long's first map was "GREAT DESERT," which became "GREAT AMERICAN DESERT" in Henry Tanner's popular *Atlas* of 1823.

Westerners paid little attention. Already a vanguard of backwoods trappers had scoured the beaver-rich canyonlands of the Snake-Columbia basin. In 1826, the *St. Louis Enquirer* maintained that wagons could reach Oregon without meeting "any obstruction deserving the name of a MOUNTAIN." The rosy assessment was confirmed in Jedediah Smith's 1830 report to Secretary of War John Eaton: families with wagons and cattle could follow the Snake to a fine country for farming. Two years later, when the French American soldier and fur trader Benjamin Bonneville took wagons over the Continental Divide into future Wyoming, expansionists rejoiced. American evangelists, stirred by frontier reports from the Presbyterian missionary Samuel Parker in 1835, claimed the road across the lava desert had been "excavated by the finger of God." On that desert passage were obstacles more political than physical. The United States and Britain held Oregon Territory jointly, although few Americans ventured north of Puget Sound. The London-based Hudson's Bay Company had long monopolized the beaver trade with a string of trade outposts and forts. Company agent John McLoughlin, the factor at Walla Walla and celebrated "father of Oregon," dismissed the idea of Yankees beyond the Rockies. Emigrants might just as well "undertake to go to the moon."

More fearsome than the British resistance were the nomadic and warlike Sioux. Displaced by white migration to the Upper Mississippi, the Sioux were highly mobile and less susceptible to smallpox than stationary tribes. By the 1840s, the Sioux had enslaved the Arikara people, scattered the Mandan, and pushed Plains Indians such as the Omaha and Cheyenne into the Blackfoot lands at the base of the Northern Rockies. Sioux warriors so devastated the Pawnee that the defeated tribe made an alliance with the U.S. Army. Although the Snake River Shoshone had no tradition of organized warfare, the tall-grass steppelands were ablaze with violence and thoroughly destabilized long before the first of the covered wagons rutted the Oregon Trail.

Missionaries first passed through Indian lands under the protection of British and American trappers. Jason Lee, a Methodist, went west in 1834 to preach among the Flathead. His mission on the Willamette River became the nucleus of the first American settlement in Oregon.

Another pioneer of the great migration was a pious Presbyterian with a degree from a New York medical school. Dr. Marcus Whitman, in 1835, won fame among the Shoshone, Nez Percé, and Flathead by removing a three-inch arrowhead from the back of mountain man Jim Bridger. The following year Whitman returned to the mountains with his schoolteacher bride, Narcissa Prentiss Whitman, and fellow husband-and-wife missionaries Henry and Eliza Spalding. On July 4, 1836, the party with its shanty wagon crossed the Continental Divide. "Were met by a large party of Nez Percés, men, women, and children," wrote Eliza Spalding in a diary entry for July 6. "All appeared happy to see us. If permitted to reach their country and locate among them, may our labors be blessed to their temporal and spiritual good." But the horse trail across the future Idaho-Wyoming border was a teamster's nightmare. On July 18, Narcissa Whitman reported that the hated wagon had flipped over twice. "It was a great wonder," she wrote, "that [the wagon] was not turning somersaults continually." When the axle broke ten days later, the schoolteacher rejoiced. The rejoicing, however, proved premature when the men converted the wagon into a makeshift cart and continued on two wheels. Still, the cart was probably the first wheeled vehicle to survive the Devil's Backbone. Although the wagon was junked for scrap at Fort Boise, the journey punctured the myth of the West as a trackless desert. There was no stopping America's greatness if missionaries—even "delicate females" as one senator put it—could undertake such a migration. In 1837 a Senate bill to protect U.S. citizens in Oregon prompted a bellicose call to evict the British from the entire 700,000 square miles of the Pacific Northwest.

A surge to the Pacific secured America's claim. On September 20, 1838, Thomas Jefferson Farnham of Peoria contracted Oregon fever from the touring Jason Lee.

Battlements of basalt near Gooding, Idaho. Left: the future Magic Valley seemed a pathless desert before the Whitman-Spalding party survived the Devil's Backbone in 1836.

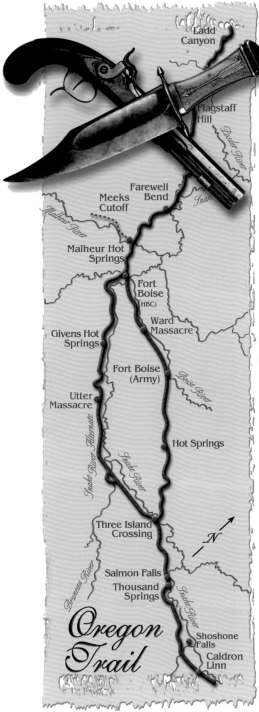

Oregon Trail

Ladd Canyon

Flagstaff Hill

Farewell Bend

Meeks Cutoff

Malheur Hot Springs

Fort Boise (HBC)

Ward Massacre

Givens Hot Springs

Fort Boise (Army)

Utter Massacre

Hot Springs

Three Island Crossing

Salmon Falls

Thousand Springs

Shoshone Falls

Caldron Linn

Farnham's Oregon Dragoons crossed the Missouri the following year with fifteen emigrants and a homemade banner that boldly proclaimed "OREGON OR THE GRAVE." The dragoons split into several detachments after suffering many hardships. Farnham, nevertheless, stirred interest in the Shoshone-Paiute country by publishing vivid reports. At Salmon Falls were "digger" Indians, "the most worthless Indians, that is poor, that we have seen." The Peorians traded three knives for "a bale" of sun-baked salmon cured "in a very fine stile." Rested and fed, they arched the Devil's Backbone and descended through rocky desert to Three Island Crossing. Farnham then followed the Shoshone trail past bubbling hot springs to the bluffs of "a very b[ea]utifull and rapid stream" with a "stony and gravelly bottom." It was the Boise River near the future town site. Again the dragoons traded for salmon and wandered through dangerously twisting canyons where, said Farnham, "our ears are yet saluted by the howl of the woolf." Soon the travelers heard human "houling."

"The most tortuous road" looped south of Salmon Falls to Three Island Crossing. Right: weary faces show the strain of the overland passage in this family portrait, about 1870.

An encampment of Bannock, apparently, were "mourning for the loss of some of their friends that had been killed in battle." Three suspended their grief long enough to point the dragoons toward Fort Boise. There in the dying days of the fur trade the Peorians feasted on duck, bacon, sturgeon, buffalo, elk, turnips, cabbage, and pickled beets at the table of the fort's famous factor, the French Canadian Francois Payette.

By 1840, some 500 Americans occupied maybe one hundred farms in and around the Willamette Valley. In 1841, legendary hunter Tom "Broken Hand" Fitzpatrick led John Bidwell and his Western Emigration Society—the first

bona fide wagon train. U.S. Topographical Engineer John C. Frémont marched west the following May with Hawkin rifles, barometers and transits, pack mules, kettles and blankets for

Indian tribute, a stout crew of French trappers, six thermometers, an inflatable rubber raft, a
soft-spoken scout named Kit Carson, and the red-faced German who became one of

America's most celebrated cartographers, Charles Preuss. Two days ahead of Frémont was Indian agent Elijah White with his emigrant company of more than one hundred children, women, and men in thirty amphibious wagons.

In 1842 the British well understood that the push through the lava desert was more than a peasant migration. Strategic intelligence in the guise of scientific reconnaissance—a tactic predating Lewis and Clark and continuing in the work of highly placed army savants such as Long, Frémont, Zebulon Pike, William H. Emory, Howard Stansbury, Andrew A. Humphreys, and Gouverneur K. Warren—ran counter to the myth of the West as the process through which Americans shed the schooled culture of seaboard civilization. Government science preceded the wagon migration. Already in 1841 the U.S. Exploring Expedition had grounded the USS *Peacock* in the crashing surf at the mouth of the Columbia River. It was a fortuitous embarrassment for American imperialism. Demonstrating the uselessness of the Columbia as a gateway to Asia, the wreck of the *Peacock* turned the attention of Congress north to safe harbor in Puget Sound.

Congress, meanwhile, stirred West Coast colonization with offers of farmland. Two decades before the Homestead Act of 1862 sent farmers flooding west, the Senate, in 1843, pledged 640 acres of Oregon Country to each male pioneer. Although the proposal died in the House, it stoked expansionist fire. Democrat James K. Polk turned the 1844 presidential election into a referendum on annexation or, if necessary, brute conquest. Challenging the British to "Fifty-four forty or fight"—a demand for every inch of disputed terrain from California to Alaska—Polk defeated moderate Henry Clay. Two years later a British-American compromise at the 49th parallel made the United States continental. Approved by the Senate on July 17, 1846, the Oregon treaty gave America its deepwater port (future Seattle) and relinquished to the British the wilds above Puget Sound.

Thousand Springs. Right: Rock Creek Station, a stage stop in 1865.

By 1846—a "year of decision," said historian Bernard DeVoto, a zealous time of "manifest destiny" when the Mormons left for Salt Lake and General Zachary Taylor decapitated northern Mexico—the overland trails were rutted and thronged. On July 17, 1850, the peak day of the migration, 6,034 emigrants crowded toward Oregon and California. James Wilkins, Missourian, noted "a great many [wagon] companies continually in sight." White-topped schooners dotted empty Nebraska "like a string of beads."

Fury & Astonishing Splendor

A braid more than a trail, the road to empire looped, sidetracked, and frayed through a tangle of byways and cutoffs. "Here we are upon a sage plain with roads running in every direction," wrote Julius Merrill, Boise-bound and short-cutting through the Camas Prairie in 1864. "We are at a loss which [road] to take."

A trace of the nineteenth-century route onto a twentieth-century map shows 492 miles across the barrens of Idaho via Three Island Crossing. Those unwilling or unable to cross that dangerous ford could detour 505 miles via the mesa lands of Idaho's Owyhee desert. In 1852 a ferry at Thousand Springs opened the Rock Creek or North Alternate Route that bypassed the Devil's Backbone via Malad Gorge. Steep and stony in any direction, Idaho was tough going—"the most tortuous road I could ever imagine," said emigrant Ester McMillan in that year. Idaho was elsewhere an "ash heap." Its serpentine river was "mad." For an emigrant to enjoy the ordeal, said one, "a man must be able to endure heat like a Salamander, mud and water like a muskrat, dust like a toad, and labor like a jackass. He must learn to eat with his unwashed fingers, drink out of the same vessel with his mules, sleep on the ground when it rains, and share his blanket with vermin, and have patience with musketoes, who don't know any difference between the face of a man and the face of a mule, but dash without ceremony from one into the other. He must cease to think, except to where he may find grass and water and a good camping place. It is hardship without glory, to be sick without a home, to die and be buried like a dog."

For many, the eighty-some miles from Caldron Linn to Three Islands (Murtaugh to Glenns Ferry) were the most difficult leg of the trip. "Hideous world, fearful roads, all grass poisoned, every day one to three head of cattle dying," wrote William

Keil in 1855. The wind-blown Idaho silt now famous for growing potatoes (geologists call it loess) could blind in the heat of August. "The dust," said emigrant Jane Gould from the Middle Snake in the summer of 1862, "was even worse than Indians, storms, or winds or

mosquitoes, or even wood ticks. Dust ... if I could just have a bath."

The excessive dust was a good indication that the cattle-invaded steppeland was an ecosystem in shock. No longer a flowering diversity of bitterroot, goldenweed, balsam, clover, rye, wild onion, and camas, the palouse had surrendered to sage. As noxious weeds such as cheatgrass and Russian thistle (tumbleweed) displaced more edible species, nature, said emigrant Overton Johnson, was "wrecked and ruined." Another witness to desolation was the twenty-one-year-old Ohio man who later returned, eastbound on the eve of his 98th birthday, to make the case for preserving segments of trail. "When the Snake River was reached," said Ezra Meeker, recalling the 1850s, "the heat again became oppressive, the dust stifling, and the thirst almost maddening. In some places we could see the water of the Snake winding through the lava gorges; but we could not reach it, as the river ran in the inaccessible depths of the canyon." The desert "scarcely afforded sustenance," said Cyrus Shepard. It was "burnt rocks ... damned bad dust ... horned toads, rattlesnakes and the damned Snake Indians," said E. S. McComas. Five decades before Twin Falls boosters imagined "fertile soil ... beautiful scenery ... [a] climate equal to Italy's best ... a new Garden of Eden," Basil Longworth of Ohio saw only "a remarkably strange place."

Remarkably strange, surely, but wondrous to tastemakers like Washington Irving who rediscovered the pastoral West as mysterious and sublime. "It is a land," wrote Irving in 1837, "where no man permanently resides; a vast, uninhabited solitude with precipitous cliffs and yawning ravines, looking like the ruins of a world: vast desert tracts that must ever defy cultivation and interpose dreary and thirsty wilds between the habitation of man." It was a land so beguiling, moreover, that many thousands of the Oregon-bound suspended the race against starvation and snowfall to stand, spellbound, on the brink of impossible chasms in the mist of plunging cascades. T. J. Farnham of Peoria, a visitor to Twin Falls in 1839, heard the boom of its crashing water from at least three miles away. Today but a trickle of its former grandeur, its water diverted upstream by plumbing for agriculture, Twin Falls of the Middle Snake once sheeted in a double torrent around a

Box Canyon on the Middle Snake. Springs replenish the Magic Valley through the basalt walls of this little-known wildlife sanctuary about twenty miles northwest of Twin Falls.

massive rock. An 1880 lithograph shows a native with raised spear sentrylike at the foot of a roaring Niagara. Taller but more remote was the future tourist attraction four miles downstream. Shoshone Falls—called Canadian Falls until the U.S. Army expunged the reference to America's rival—fell 212 feet into a hollow amphitheater where a whirl of the Bonneville Flood left a ruin of fractured basalt. Known to trappers and traders but inaccessible by emigrant wagon, Shoshone Falls remained outside the geography of American science until U.S. Geologist Clarence King took a photographer to Idaho in 1868. King reported "a strange, savage scene: a monotony of pale-blue sky, olive and gray stretches of desert, frowning walls of jetty lava, deep beryl-green of river-stretches, reflecting, here and there, the intense solemnity of the cliffs, and in the centre a dazzling sheet of foam."

Emigrants turned from the brink as if, said King, "from a frightful glimpse of the Inferno," but soon the vision had vanished and the stillness of sagebrush reigned. At trail mile 1,327 a willow-matted ravine called Rock Creek provided the first accessible water since the emigrants left Caldron Linn. Here in 1864 outfitter John Bascom built a lava rock stage station on the future Kelton Road. Bascom soon added a general store with a sod-roofed cellar and squarish Old West verandah—now the oldest building in southcentral Idaho. Here also was the saloon where a grocery clerk cut down outlaw Bill Dowdle in one of Idaho's famous shootouts. A nearby cave held the first jail in Twin Falls County until a federal statute made it illegal to keep prisoners underground.

A sugar factory and water treatment plant now flank the Rock Creek Crossing west of Twin Falls. Along a prehistoric trail well used by the buffalo hunters, wagons looped north to the rim of the Snake and, if the salmon were running, one of the journey's most thrilling views. Here in May or June the Chinook returned by the countless thousands to challenge Kanaka Rapids. And here below thundering springs were dams and dikes of boulders and brush that

Shoshone chiefs pose with Chief Washakie (front row center). Known as "the Friend of the White Man," Washakie was a proud diplomat of the Shoshone and an inspirational visionary for cooperation among races.

diverted the leaping salmon through a gauntlet of fishing pools. "Fish rise in such multitudes that the Indians can pierce them with their spears without looking," said mapmaker Preuss. Shoshone-Paiute journeyed from as far as Oregon and Wyoming to fish for steelhead trout in the spring and Chinook in the early summer. Buffalo hunters rode west from Fort Hall en route to the Camas Prairie. Horseless Northern Paiute descended from the Nevada highlands. Armed with nets, hooks, stone axes, and double-

Despite claims that Indians were exterminated, Shoshone survived. Late-nineteenth-century portraits from top: Sego, Chief Oiti, and Washakie's grandson. Right: baby on board—Mary Enos with cradleboard, about 1884.

pronged fishing spears, the natives took mountains of fish. Applegate in 1843 saw among willow huts "something red in color." Scarlet strips of drying fish hung everywhere like laundry on lines.

A thousand springs freshened this trenchlike reach of the Snake, its canyons diked and piled with refuge from the Bonneville Flood. Rifleman Osborne Cross saw in these weeping fissures "a singular freak of nature." Frémont embellished: "A subterranean river bursts out directly from the face of the escarpment, and falls in white foam to the river below." On October 1, 1843, under the curious gaze of "good nature[d]" and "unusually gay savages," Frémont set out in a rubber raft to study the foam at its thundering source. Ten miles upriver from Kanaka Rapids (called "Fishing Falls" in Frémont's journal) was "a picturesque spot of singular beauty." Bursting like broken plumbing in the canyon's northern wall were two crystalline springs that rushed together and fell 160 feet onto rocks whitened by saline. Blue water hugged vertical cliffs like a flowing apron. At 58°F, the blue spring water measured seven degrees warmer than the river's silvery snowmelt. Nearby on a slope dense with cane and poison nettles, the engineer collected shells "of small crustacea" said to be evidence of a freshwater sink in the neighboring highlands. Frémont was essentially right: Crystal Springs, as it came to be called, was snow-fed through a sink of the Lost River in the lava beds north of Fort Hall.

Emigrant impressions were mixed and less scientific. Guidebook author William H. Winter saw Thousand Springs from a distance and imagined "banks of snow resting on the cliffs." Longsworth of Ohio described "a most pleasing and sublime spectacle." Jason Lee praised the divine: tumbling springs, icy white, ran with "impetuous fury and astonishing splendor down the rugged banks. ... How astonishing are the works of God."

And how astonishing the works of Man at trail mile 1,366 where a dozen squat Indian lodges or "wigwams" resembled a willow grove. The seasonal "village" at Upper Salmon Falls commanded the head of a roiling staircase between two sets of rapids about five miles apart. "The river on this [southwest] side and all the islands are lined with shanties and black with Indians," wrote Theodore Talbot of Missouri, a greenhorn in the Frémont party. "These Indians," Talbot continued, "speak the same language as the other Snakes but are far poorer." Copper-skinned, they were "low in stature and ill-made." Some wore groundhog skins with a vest or maybe a shirt bartered from an emigrant's wagon. Others were "entirely naked." The women had "thick crooked legs." The men had "bad eyes." Preuss called them "miserable" but "happy" and "harmless." W. H. Winter of Indiana reported natives "so poor and feeble [in winter] that they frequently die from actual starvation." In summer, however, "they [were] fat as penned pigs, ... the fattest, most depraved, and degraded creatures anywhere to be found among the dregs of human nature."

Happy, harmless, isolated, depraved—the Shoshone at Salmon Falls seemed the Lockean ideal of natural man untouched by civilization. Only now are Americans beginning to see how traumas exported from Europe had preceded the wagon invasion. How blights such as smallpox and measles had decimated indigenous peoples. How northern Shoshone had been displaced by Blackfoot fleeing the Sioux who had crossed the Mississippi to escape farmers in Minnesota. How the catalytic horse, returning to Idaho via Mexico, had suddenly enriched and empowered societies such as the Oregon Bannock who now hunted at the base of the Tetons and pastured in the Hagerman Valley. How a fad for beaver hats had forever changed the stream hydrology of the Shoshone country by eradicating the backwater pools impounded by beaver dams. Already the natives of the Middle Snake had been thoroughly shaken, their cultures remade, by people and microbes in motion. Stereotypes deceived.

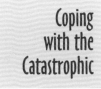

Coping with the Catastrophic

The Snake River Shoshone-Bannock, need it be said, were not peaceful or warlike or feeble or fat but human and idiosyncratic. Ethnically diverse and a marble of many cultures, they responded to the wagon invasion in contradictory ways. Some resisted. Some accommodated. Some died in the crossfire or fled.

Never, however, were they unconditionally defeated. To reduce their history to "one horror after another endured by the reds at the hands of the whites" would be to slight the leverage

Shoshone warrior with tomahawk and fur pelt necklace, 1884.

of armed resistance, converting the marauding savage to the passive victim in an exchange of stereotypes. To say that "the progress of the white settlers meant the death of the Indians" would be to forget some 9,000 Idaho-Nevada Sho-Ban who remain ethnically independent enough to be counted by the U.S. Census. To flatly declare that "Native Americans were exterminated" would be to deny the Indian the most pervasively human of frontier characteristics—the capacity to cope.

Marauding savage and passive victim once coexisted in the mythology of the road that conquered the West. In 1843, for example, the dour German who traveled with Frémont thought the bounty of Thousand Springs made the natives too complacent for Christ. "Wealth," wrote Preuss of the Salmon Eaters, "makes them insolent and arrogant, as it does the Sioux." For George Catlin, however, the lords of the Far West prairie were incapable of insolence. A lawyer-turned-artist who visited the western Shoshone in 1855, Catlin saw behind Indian eyes "a beautiful blank upon which anything could be written." Indians "had no business hours to attend or professions to learn." They had "no notes in the bank or other debts to pay—no taxes, no tithes, no rent." Why, then, should Christian man bother to convert and conquer? Because romantics like Catlin knew all things wild would perish, and also because even an artist could see the Great American Desert was richer than once imagined. Crystal Springs, said an emigrant in 1853, was "large enough to turn machinery." Thousand Springs, said another, had "mill sites enough for the whole state of Illinois."

Nowhere were the prisms of misunderstanding more culturally distorted than in the barter for goods and services so vital to the Oregon Trail. Maj. Osborne Cross of the U.S. Regiment of Mounted Riflemen pondered the "degenerate" state of primitive man after trading at Salmon Falls. Why had the Salmon Eaters haggled so doggedly for "an old tin cup, partly without a bottom." And why were two rifle cartridges worth more than a woolen blanket? Perhaps these people bartered for sport or, said Cross, "simply to gratify their fancy." Shirts were especially valuable. "Father took the shirt off his back in exchange for a big fish," Clarence Bagley remembered. Metal fishhooks were another popular item. On August 21, 1851, an emigrant bartered a hook for a monstrous fish "as long as a wagon b[e]d." It was enough fish "to make us wish never to see any more." Often the market was glutted. "Dull sale," Cecilia Adams remarked after Indians tried for a second day to unload a basket of glistening salmon.

Markets pitched and fell in a rudderless commerce without the ballast of a shared legal tradition or a common ethical code. What legality governed ownership and access to prairie resources? Was it stealing to gather wood? To forage and hunt? Indeed it was, said Chief Washakie of the Wind River Shoshone. "This country," the chief reminded his people, "was once covered with buffalo, elk, deer and antelope, and we had plenty to eat, and also robes for bedding, and to make lodges." Born in Sacagawea's village a year before Lewis and Clark arrived, he had come of age on buffalo hunts at the base of the Grand Tetons during an era of unprecedented prosperity for Plains Indians suddenly enriched by the horse. "But now," he protested in 1855, "since the white man has made a road across our land, and has killed off our game, we are hungry. ... Our women and children cry for food and we have no food to give them." Where the historian Turner lauded that frontier process, Washakie saw devastation: the cattle grazing that crushed edible roots and seeds so vital to Shoshone subsistence, the gold hysteria that stripped forests and pockmarked the hills, releasing mudslides. More ruinous still were the sportsmen and trophy hunters. Twenty-five million buffalo had roamed west of the Mississippi before horses and firearms. In 1883 a museum expedition searched the Plains for a healthy specimen. Less than 200 remained.

A cavalryman holds a carbine with a buckhorn sight, 1880s.

Emigrants of good conscience denounced the barbarous slaughter. Should a horse go missing, however, Indians were condemned. In 1851 a pioneer lost a horse, suspected theft, crouched behind a rock where Shoshone were lancing salmon, and shot an Indian dead. Nearby at Rock Creek that same year an emigrant company arrived to find Sho-Ban peacefully camped. The wagon master blasted a shotgun while his men charged cavalry-style. The next day a war party shot three emigrants, killing one.

Arrogant treatment continued because the risk of retribution was small. Historian John Unruh has shown that the danger of Indian ambush has been greatly exaggerated, that more Indians than whites died in these confrontations, and that red-on-white violence accounted for less than four percent of emigrant deaths. Murder, indeed, was rare, but raids on livestock were common near Salmon Falls. Historian Donald Shannon's chronology of "Snake country massacres" shows nineteen attacks on emigrant trains before 1863. Ten erupted within one hundred miles of the Devil's Backbone. Idaho, moreover, was the killing ground of the trail's most sensational carnage. Of the very few "non-mythical trail tragedies" large enough to make Unruh's selective list of "real massacres," the two most horrific involved Shoshone-Paiute who allegedly fished and pastured in the Hagerman Valley. Said Col. George Wright, the Oregon District commander at Fort Vancouver, "those [Indians] who are more hostile are near Salmon Falls."

Horse trading gone bad may have been the spark that ignited the first confrontation lopsided enough to deserve Snake Country "massacre" status. On August 19, 1854, about thirty miles north of the Devil's Backbone where Goodale's cutoff dissected the Camas Prairie, eleven Sho-Ban approached a wagon train, demanded horses, and opened fire. Three emigrants died. Survivors said the attackers were "Winnestah Snakes" (mounted Shoshone) from Salmon Falls. Historians speculate that the attack was connected to an altercation of the previous day in which wagon master Alexander Ward of Lexington, Missouri, had tracked horses to a Sho-Ban camp near the future city of Boise. Ward and his men retrieved the horses, presumably at gunpoint. By midday on August 20, a war party of thirty or more had overtaken Ward as his five-wagon detachment crossed the Boise Valley near the future farm town of Middleton. A warrior jumped on a horse. Guns blazed. Thirty Indians charged. Two days later the rescuers found among blackened wagons the widely scattered remains of nineteen pioneers. The wife of the wagon master had been ravaged with a hot poker. Three children were missing and another three, a newsman reported, "had doubtless been burnt alive, and the mother forced to witness it." Outraged editorialists called for an "everlasting treaty" of genocidal retribution. Sixty-five federal troops arrived the following spring, corralled about 200 Indians, tried and convicted four, shot one, and at nightfall on July 18, 1855, noosed the remaining three to a gallows at the massacre site. Soldiers cut down the bodies at daybreak. The gallows, however, remained.

The Oregon-bound faced a graver danger from accidental shootings than Indian attacks. Above: 1860 "old wrist breaker" cavalry saber; pre–Civil War flintlock pistol. Left: Fort Boise Gatling gun (replica), 1883.

Idaho's second "massacre" began in late August 1860 when a one-eyed white man and two Indian companions tracked a forty-four-emigrant train from Rock Creek to Salmon Falls. Wagon master Elijah Utter (or "Otter" as historians have misspelled it) suspected the rough-looking three were spies. "We bought some dried salmon of them and hurried away," said Emeline Trimble, the daughter of Utter's new wife. Age 13 in 1860, she had already lost her father to typhoid fever and the middle finger of her left hand to an accident with an axe. While riding in her stepfather's wagon, she had also lost part of an eye to a flying nail, but she was observant: the white man, apparently the leader, had a torn white hat, a thick stubble on his upper lip, and long hair pulled over his bad eye. His face was brown with war paint. One night the sinister trio "came to our wagon and pretended to be glad to see us." The pioneers consulted and "thought the safest way would be to kill them, but [we] hardly dared do so for fear of being found out by the Indians." Instead the wagon train fled via the Devil's Backbone. Seven days later, again with an axe, Trimble would fend off the one-eyed man and other attackers, escaping through the cover of sagebrush. "I often wish we had done as our better judgement had told us and killed them," wrote Trimble in *Left by the Indians*, her account of the gruesome event.

The attack began Hollywood style. About 10 A.M. on September 9, 1860, at mile 1,450 on the South Alternate Route in the slabbed and terraced barrens of future Owyhee County, an Indian horseman in breechcloth and feathered headdress led one hundred braves against eight encircled wagons. Arrows tore canvas. Bullets and firebrands rained intermittently for thirty hours as emigrants dug in behind a breastwork of trail supplies. Charles Utter of Wisconsin, a towheaded lad of twelve or thirteen and an excellent marksman, killed five charging attackers as fast as he could reload. The wagon circle held until an hour before dusk on the second day when four of the defenders—all ex-soldiers who had fallen in with the Utters, promising protection for food—galloped toward the western mountains with emigrant horses and guns. Twenty overlanders and perhaps thirty Indians died or were mortally wounded in two days of withering combat. Three of the four deserters later fell in a mountain ambush. Eighteen pioneers escaped.

Col. Wright's 1860 report from the Oregon Country had already boasted "complete success in the protection of the immigration route." Now Wright thought he was fighting a phantom. "We have no fixed objective," Wright wrote on October 11, 1860. "We pursue an invisible foe, without a home or anything tangible to strike at." The best the army could do was dispatch a one hundred–troops relief force from Walla Walla. Second Lt. Marcus A. Reno—later martyred with General George Armstrong Custer at Little Bighorn—led forty dragoons to Farewell Bend near Huntington, Oregon, where the young officer discovered six of the eighteen who had escaped five weeks before. Reno found them "gleaming in the moonlight, dead, stripped, and mutilated." Closer to the original massacre site were twelve others who had survived mostly on moss and the flesh of four dead emigrant children. Frostbitten and muttering blankly after forty-five days of exposure, the living were "raving mad."

Textiles talk. U.S. regimental flag carried through the Indian wars (top). Shoshone blanket romanticized in a 1913 Capps & Sons catalog.

The Salmon Falls Massacre (so named in 1860 by survivor Joseph Myers; also called the Sinker Creek Massacre and the Otter–Van Orman Massacre) erupted six days and seventy-nine trail miles west of the Devil's Backbone in a desert too remote for a more accurate place-name. Twenty-two months elapsed before Abraham Lincoln's army could properly search for the marauders and the four children allegedly kidnapped. At last in August 1862, the First Oregon Cavalry reached what Lt. Col. Rueben F. Maury called "the principal haunt of the Snake Indians." Here at Salmon Falls, according to an army informant, a council of chiefs had recently divided over whether or not to make war on emigrant trains. But the Oregonians found no war council, only an encampment of impoverished natives too "miserable" to attack. Searching from Bruneau Canyon to Twin Falls in the summer of 1863, the cavalry "collected" about forty Shoshone who "had no arms and a very small number of Indian ponies," and who "expressed great desire for peace and a willingness to do anything or go anywhere they might be directed." Maury insisted that "something should be done" with these fishing people lest they be "punished for the depredations of the roaming and more enterprising bands."

An American soldier of another sort was meanwhile too impatient for distinctions among Indian cultures and types. "Leave their bodies thus exposed as an example of what evildoers might expect," said Col. Patrick E. Connor of the California Volunteers. "You [the troops] will also destroy every male Indian who you may encounter. ... I desire that the order may be rigidly enforced." Shooting Shoshone on sight as his army marched eastward from Sacramento to Camp Douglas above Salt Lake City, Connor spoiled for combat. It came on the subzero morning of January 29, 1863, at Battle Creek off the Bear River north of Franklin, Idaho. Connor allegedly yelled "Kill everything—nits make lice" as 300 volunteers with two howitzers opened fire on a seventy-tepee encampment. Four hours of methodical fire killed an estimated 368 Shoshone, including perhaps ninety women and children. Twenty-two soldiers died.

It was the bloodiest slaughter of Indians on record in the history of the American West. With a body count more than double the Sioux dead at Wounded Knee (146) or the Cheyenne dead at Sand Creek (130), the Battle of Bear River remains all the more tragic

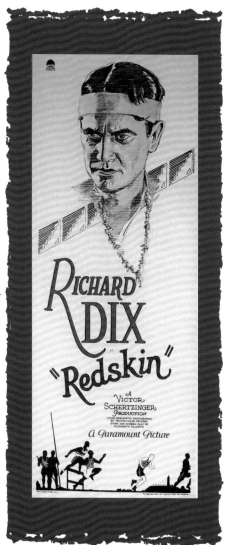

Paramount's *Redskin*, 1929.

because its tale is rarely told. In the 1974 edition of *Westward Expansion*, a standard college-level textbook, famed historian Ray Allen Billington reduced the Shoshone resistance to a single, inaccurate sentence: "[In 1868] Shoshoni and Bannock tribes ceded their lands in return for annuities and two small reservations." More recently, Jon E. Lewis's *Mammoth Book of the West* finds space for Buffalo Bill's funeral and outlaw Butch Cassidy's escape to South America but none for the army's final solution to attacks on the

Oregon Trail. Perhaps Idaho remains too remote for the publishers of history textbooks. Or perhaps Idahoans prefer the brevity of William Ghent's account in *Road to Oregon*: "The weather was bitterly cold and [Colonel Connor's] men suffered greatly. ... [Connor] attacked the Indian camp on Bear River, near the present Franklin, Idaho, killing most of three hundred warriors and capturing 160 women and children. For this feat, which brought peace, cleared the Trail, and opened to settlement a region that had been harassed for fifteen years, Connor was made a brigadier general of volunteers."

Alas the hapless savage. Peace and progress required a crushing defeat—or so Ghent contended in 1929. A poem published in Boise the following year bled for the "brave pioneers" who "suffered woe/ to bring the frontier westward ho." The poet continued:

> They braved dangers ever near,
> In early days of Idaho.
> Ah, who can say they did not fear—
> In Idaho, our Idaho—
> To meet the dusky, hidden foe,
> With poison dart and trusted bow,
> Whose purpose was to lay them low,
> In Idaho, our Idaho?

Poison darts? So fogged was the road to empire that historians ignored the Shoshone resistance until the United States Army was again chasing a hidden foe through the jungles of Vietnam. Not until the late 1960s and 1970s did historians such as Merle Wells and Brigham Madsen begin to understand that the killing of Shoshone noncombatants accomplished about as much as the carpet bombing of Hanoi: it infuriated the enemy, redoubling the will to resist.

POST-OFFICE, JARBIDGE.
COPYRIGHT, 1910- BY AMOS STUDIO
TWIN FALLS,
IDA

"Instead of cowing the Northwestern Shoshoni," wrote Madsen, "there is overwhelming evidence that the reverse happened." In 1863, for example, a twenty-warrior attack near the boom town of Bannock City (future Idaho City) killed the gold miner who discovered the mother lode, George Grimes. Michael Jordon, the prospector who found gold in the Owyhees, met the same brutal fate. The emigrant road from Rock Creek Station to the ferry at Salmon Falls became a target of Sho-Ban resistance, frequently raided for livestock. In 1865 a battle near Rock Creek suspended stage service and left three Indians dead.

Violence trapped the Salmon Eaters like wayfarers battered by storm. More than 400 Shoshone from various places spent the bitter winter of 1867–68 under armed guard at a refugee camp near Boise. But no trail of tears forced the refugees to abandon ancestral homelands. When the army in 1869 attempted to caravan the refugees to the new Fort Hall Shoshone-Bannock Indian Reservation, most dispersed into trackless canyons. When again in 1877 the U.S. Indian Bureau used "every possible means" to entice "homeless" nomads to a second Sho-Ban reservation at Duck Valley in the Owyhee highlands, two-thirds refused to go. Some returned to the Hagerman Valley under the protection of friendly whites. For decades they ranched, sold baskets, worked the ferries, fished the seasonal salmon, camped along the river, and learned the ways of the whites without forsaking all tradition. When Swan Falls Dam opened without fish ladders in 1902, they subsisted on suckers and trout.

"The Shoshone had little to lose," wrote anthropologist Peter Farb in an essay that tried to explain why horseless nomads were spared the wrenching dislocation experienced by other Indian groups. For centuries they had purposefully migrated from resource to resource without trade goods or military escort or even the pretense of sole ownership to any particular place. Warfare reduced the Shoshone-Paiute to the bare minimum of human existence—a familiar state. Acculturating without assimilating, the fishing people of the Middle Snake acknowledged the emigrant's world without forsaking native religion or language and without conceding defeat. Thus they weathered the Oregon Trail in much the same way their ancestors had braved the trauma of smallpox or the ecological ravage of lava flows and floods. They coped with the catastrophic, adapting to survive.

Stand at Hagerman

"Stand at the Cumberland Gap," said Frederick Jackson Turner, "and watch the procession of civilization, marching single file—the buffalo following the trail to the salt springs, the Indian, the fur-trader and hunter, the cattle-raiser, the pioneer farmer—and the frontier has passed by." Turner continued: "Stand at the South Pass in the Rockies a century later and see the same procession with wider intervals between." Stand at Hagerman and deconstruct that linear progress. See not one society consuming another but strata upon strata of human experience, not a process remaking a nation but a homeland, an actual place.

Stand where Applegate stood and see the historical importance of a ridge more famously known for fossils of megafauna. Much has changed. An Idaho Power Company dam has silenced Salmon Falls, reducing Class III rapids to an annual generating capacity of 60,000 kilowatts. Likewise the fury that so astonished John C. Frémont and Clarence King at Shoshone Falls and Thousand Springs can today best be appreciated by flicking a light switch in Salt Lake City or Seattle. But the mystery of the steppeland remains atop the Devil's Backbone where sandy soil preserves a metallic record of rings, rims, pins, chains, and square nails of the sort that partially blinded farm girl Emeline Trimble. The Hagerman Fossil Beds National Monument is one of only three park service sites with Oregon Trail remnants. Largely undeveloped and undiscovered by vandals, the torturous grade preserves in its

Detail, Frank Tenney Johnson's *Oregon or California* (1926).

graveyard of broken hardware a maze of trails and cutoffs. Some are straight and rutted with hardship enough to support the well-worn mythology of the West as America's triumph. "The blazing of the Old Oregon Trail will stand forever as one of the greatest achievements of man," said Boise's *Capital News* as moviegoers packed the Egyptian Theater to watch John Wayne kill Indians for civilization in the 1930 release of *The Big Trail*. Other trails, however, resemble the historical record: faint and distorted, a progression thoroughly twisted by what Americans choose to forget.

"How did the United States get title to Shoshone territory?" asks Raymond Yowell of Elko, Nevada. Black hat, silver hair, a U.S. Air Force veteran who heads the Western Shoshone National Council on the Duck Valley Reservation, he fights the government still. "If you say we've been conquered, show us where the battle took place. Show us the terms of surrender and show us the signatures of the Shoshone chiefs who signed the papers."

Yowell is right historically speaking. And wrong. No juggernaut rolled in from the East to smash his civilization. In the battle for historical understanding, however, the Sho-Ban's defeat was a rout. So completely was history conquered that Americans cheered when President Herbert Hoover lopped thirteen years off a century to make 1930 the official "centennial" of the 1843 Oregon Trail. Boiseans celebrated on June 12, 1930, with a day of horseshoes and baseball. At dusk the festivities closed with what the souvenir program called "an exact historical reproduction of an emigrant train being attacked by Indians and their timely rescue by a troop of United States Cavalry uniformed in authentic military style of 1860." Whooping savages fled before soldiers on polo ponies. The phantom had been vanquished at last.

◆

◆ **Ronald L. james, M.A.**
Hagerman Fossil Beds National Monument
Bob Willhite
Chief Ranger
Hagerman Fossil Beds National Monument
Todd Shallat, Ph.D.
History, Boise State University

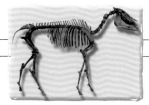
Staking Claim

CHAPTER SIX

n the schoolyard across from the post office, in Almo in Cassia County, a granite monument marks the single-most murderous ambush in the history of the overland trails. "ALMO, IDAHO," the monument reads, "DEDICATED TO THOSE WHO LOST THEIR LIVES IN A MOST HORRIBLE INDIAN MASSACRE 1861." Historians say that here below City of Rocks an attack began Indian-fashion with firebrands and hair-raising yells. Three hundred pioneers defended sixty wagons for three punishing days. Cut off from Almo Creek and desperate for water in the sun-beaten wagon enclosure, the defenders dug makeshift wells. Five pioneers escaped. One courageous young woman took a goat trail to safety at Brigham City, Utah, fleeing one hundred miles. Another scrambled on hands and knees while carrying, in her teeth, an infant suspended by swaddling clothes. Rescuers found charred wagons and 295 bodies. Tragically, wrote homesteader-historian Charles Shirley Walgamott, who heard the details from a Utah trapper, "the bodies of the unfortunate people were buried in the wells which they had dug."

Historians call it the worst disaster in Idaho history. "Red barbarity ... perhaps the most horrible and wanton slaughter of all," wrote Merrill D. Beal of Pocatello in a scholarly book on the pioneers. Larry Quinn's 1996 *A History of the Magic Valley* upped the body count to 300 and added: "The attackers took scalps and mutilated the bodies of men, women, and children." Marauders fresh from the kill then terrorized northern Utah with, according to Quinn, "scalps raised on poles and hung from bridles." Here, surely, was carnage crimson enough to quell revisionist sobbing over the fate of the dispossessed. If only the U.S. Indian Service had filed a report. If only a survivor had published a memoir. If only Salt Lake's *Deseret News* or any other frontier paper, all hungry for massacre stories, had mentioned the slaughter of 295 emigrants at Almo Creek. None did.

No paper reported the massacre because it never happened. Not in Cassia County. Not anywhere on the emigrant trails.

Like much good fiction, however, the massacre story stems from seeds of historical truth. It was true, for example, that Cassia County was the homeland of a fierce Shoshone named Pocatello who sacked wagons near American Falls. It was true, moreover, that Almo cowered below Silent City of Rocks—a stage station on the Kelton Road in the 1860s and as bad a badland as any on the overland trails. Here in 1860 a bold attacker in war paint had highjacked an entire wagon. The bandit, said the *Deseret News*, had "fine boots ... a pair of pants ... [and] spoke to the cattle in good English."

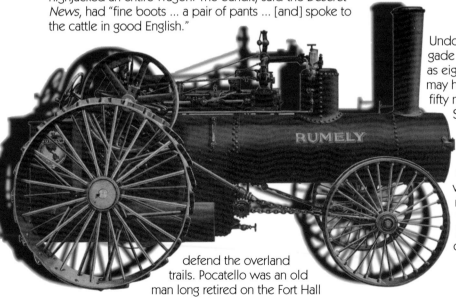

Undoubtedly a renegade white. As many as eight emigrants may have died within fifty miles of the Silent City from 1860 to 1862. But Lee's surrender to Grant sent westward a mounted wave that established regional camps to defend the overland trails. Pocatello was an old man long retired on the Fort Hall

Reservation by the time Latter-day Saints from Toole, Utah, homesteaded near Oakley Station in 1879.

Utah's "'79ers" also reached the flowering sea at the base of the Sawtooths, the Camas Prairie. Here a decade before, the Treaty of Fort Bridger had surrendered the camas lands as a refuge for the Idaho Bannock. In May 1878, Bannock hunters returned to the refuge to find meadows trampled by emigrant livestock. Worse, the succulent camas had been rooted by wallowing hogs.

Kelton Station south of Silent City of Rocks, a likely place for an ambush. Left: a steam-powered thresher, about 1910. Previous: horses flatten their ears against the chugging thump of mechanized threshing, 1910.

"Starvation is staring them in the face," wrote General George Crook, a sympathetic Indian fighter. Already a chief called Buffalo Horn had bolted the Fort Hall reservation with 200-some rifled warriors. In late May the rebels swept west—sinking ferries, sacking homesteads, pillaging King Hill. On June 8, at South Mountain below Silver City, Buffalo Horn died in a hail of bullets as he charged entrenched volunteers. The Bannock regrouped and fled to the Oregon desert. General Oliver O. Howard gave chase with 800 troops. In August 1878, their mountain hideout betrayed by rival Chief Umapine of the Oregon Umatilla, the rebel commanders were ambushed under the army's white flag of truce. "Such an act of treachery toward their own race remains without a known parallel," wrote R. Ross Arnold, a historian of the Indian wars.

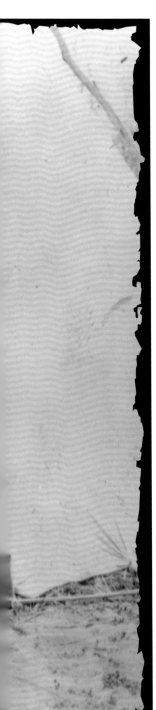

By then the Bannock homeland was wide-open cattle country. In 1872, A. J. "Barley" Harrell reached the Nevada-Idaho line with more than 3,000 Texas longhorns. Eight years later the *Idaho Tri-Weekly Statesman* counted 170,000 head in and around Rock Creek. From 1870 to 1880, meanwhile, Idaho's sheep population jumped from 1,021 to 27,326. Freight and stage entrepreneur John Hailey herded a large flock from Boise through the Camas Prairie to Big Wood River where, in 1881, he platted the town that still bears his name. Another visionary and Idaho place-name was sheepman Frank Gooding. A founder of the Idaho Wool Growers Association, Gooding, with brothers Fred and Thomas, imported a meaty breed of Kentucky merino that thrived on the north-side steppe. "There is a fine market and good outlet for anything that can be raised," said a north-side booster in 1885. Here "a poor man with little means but plenty of spirit and 'go-aheadativeness' soon surrounds himself with all the comforts of life."

The most marginal Idaho farmland required the tallest of tales. No matter the killing frost or grasshopper infestations. No matter the crickets that followed the 'hoppers to finish off drought-stricken crops. Idaho was "bright and warm" and "conducive to a cheerful and hopeful feeling which is a great aid in overcoming disease," wrote Robert Strahorn, a newsman for the Union Pacific who headed its publicity bureau.

Fables were communal identity. Common purpose. Shared hope. The Union Pacific told farmers that "grains, vegetables and fruit [would] grow in profusion" in barrens of wind-swept sagebrush. "Put money into commercial ventures, real estate, mines or live stock" because, said an Idaho booster, "heavy immigration will enhance the value of such property to a degree not now possible to comprehend." In 1885 the territorial comptroller told the story of Squire Abbott, a Camas Prairie farmer. An acre of Abbott's potatoes yielded 250 bushels without irrigation. A pound of Abbott's seed pro-

An Oakley cowboy. Left: A Bannock matriarch (said to be 117-years old) poses with daughter and grandchildren.

duced one hundred pounds of wheat. Another story of magical landscapes had a New England man in a field of melon boulders. Having paid a ridiculous $200,000 for 200 untillable acres, the New Englander turned over a boulder to find a highwayman's stolen strongbox with $125,000 in gold. A month later, while drilling a well east of Shoshone, the man sunk a shaft into an open chamber. Remarkably he had discovered the golden center of the Lost McElmore Mine.

To lure the Union Pacific through snowdrifts and melon boulders, the tales had to be tall. After 1869 the railroad giant had stalled at Ogden, Utah. Exhausted and scandal-ridden, the company languished until 1874 when investors handed the throttle to Jay Gould of New York. Gould, a self-made railroad baron who fancied himself "the most hated man in America," incorporated the Oregon Short Line as a subsidiary of the Union Pacific. Racing west from Granger, Wyoming, and spanning the Snake four times en route to a Portland connection at Huntington, Oregon, the Short Line added more than 600 miles to the Union Pacific system from 1881 to 1884.

Sometime in February 1883 the valley's first iron horse snorted past shanty tents in a place called Junction City. Locals hoping for tourists renamed the tent city Shoshone. Here Idaho gained railroading fame for beer conveniently chilled in nearby Shoshone Ice Caves. Famed also for gunfights and brawls, Shoshone City boasted a graveyard in which every headstone but one, according to Idaho legend, marked some kind of violent death. "Ten to fifteen arrests per day were common," wrote Carrie Strahorn, wife of newsman Robert. Gunmen stood guard over prisoners in an open hole. "Lot jumpers were numerous," Strahorn continued, "bad whiskey was unlimited, dancehalls were on every corner, guns were fired at all hours, and the loud time from gambling dens was ever vibrating through the air." Shoshone with its Rail Street saloons was Mecca for fargo players; also for

Comstockers from the Sierra Nevada, carpet-bagged peddlers from "Bossy City," Scandinavian maidens looking for farm work, fallen women from neighboring gold camps, Italians, Irish, Jews, Greeks, Chinese, Basque sheepherders, Mormon farm boys, frock-coated railroad attorneys, and a natty dresser named Pinkston who ran sin in the bawdy town.

Shoshone with its roundhouse and machine shops was also the transit point for the seventy-mile Wood River rail spur to Bellevue, Hailey, and Ketchum. Bellevue, called "Gate City," boomed with more than 2,000 citizens, blacksmiths, a telegraph, and a Methodist church in 1883. Hailey, by then, had two breweries, a Cy Jacobs dry goods emporium, a Wells Fargo freight depot, a First National Bank of Idaho, and a Nelson-McClintock-Dorsey-Banfield "horse restaurant" where, said *The Idaho Statesman*, "your dumb brute may be fed or starved to order, just as you desire, and where carriages, buggies, phaetons and conveyances of any kind may be had for moonlight rides through the winding canyons." Ketchum at the end of the line had a twenty-kilowatt, 125-volt dynamo-driven

smelter that electrified Idaho mining just two years after Thomas Edison patented the electric lightbulb.

Rails conquered distance without shaking myths of progress that legitimized dubious claims. Long after the silver played out and Gould lost control of the Oregon Short Line, the Middle Snake desert remained "this land of promise and fulfillment" where, said engineers, the resolute would "realize progress" and "lay the foundations of a great Commonwealth." Through fables the children of those pioneers created what folklorist Barre Toelkin has called "a blood bond with the land." Fables made a virtue of racial violence—increasingly a tragic but inevitable and therefore justifiable result of the frontier process, a cutthroat moral necessity in Idaho's masculine West. Thus the predator-pioneer "clubbed the desert and made it grow" in a 1928 poem by Idaho's Vardis Fisher. John Ryan of Camas County, Fisher's contemporary, used the same kind of brutish folklore in a loosely autobiographical compendium of man-against-nature tales. Pioneers were "soldiers of peace" in Ryan's regional memoir. "When the soldier of peace assaults the wilderness, no bugles sound the charge. The forests, the deserts, the wild beasts, the savages, the malaria, and fatigue are the foes who lurk to ambush him, and if against unequal odds he fails"—as did Ryan's own father and uncle when felled by tuberculosis—"no vollies are fired above him. The pitiless world merely sponges his name from the slate."

Shoshone caboose. Right: Oregon Short Line locomotive eastbound from Bliss, 1938. Previous: wall-stenciled street advertisements in Oakley and Shoshone; a sheep "blading crew" near Hagerman, about 1910.

Likewise the Almo dead stayed nameless and nearly forgotten until, more than seven decades since the massacre that never happened, the town had a slate engraved. It was 1938, a bad year in Cassia County. Farmers wanted federal aid for Snake River water projects. The Oakley Chamber of Commerce thirsted for tourist dollars from national monument status for the nearby City of Rocks. Idaho's Sons and Daughters of the Pioneers, meanwhile, sponsored historical essays, collected donations, and invited President Roosevelt and First Lady Eleanor to the wilds of Cassia County for a gala publicity stunt. FDR sent his regrets. But on the chill morning of October 17, 1938, the governor, a senator, a Union Pacific official, and the superintendent of Yellowstone National Park huddled among reporters in the schoolyard across from the post office in Almo where a six-foot memorial headstone—slate gray and shaped like the state of Idaho—was solemnly unveiled. Today the monument stands unaltered in tribute to magical landscapes, its story as telling as any in the lore of the homesteader's West.

Sluicing the Snake

The 1861 Massacre at Almo Creek had yet to be invented when the first wave of placer miners swept through the Middle Snake. Historians estimate a high tide of 3,000 to 4,000 miners from 1870 to 1874. Rumor-driven, treaty blind, inherently violent, and predominately male, the fever was sudden but fleeting. Skittish mineral prices and ever more golden places guaranteed boom and bust. Unlike California, however, where mining ditches and flumes quickly became the infrastructure of irrigated agriculture, the rugged basin of the Middle Snake stayed sparsely populated. In 1890, the year of Idaho statehood, the U.S. Census found barely 3,000 souls dotted in ranching hamlets through a region larger than Belgium. Hailey-born poet Ezra Pound disparaged a cultural desert 5,000 miles above sea level "and five million or thousand miles from ANYwhere, let alone from civilization" long after mining's decline.

No one knows for certain who found the first Snake River gold. Memoirist Charles Walgamott recalled that two off-duty stage drivers discovered placer gold deposits near Shoshone Falls in the fall of 1869. Boise's *The Idaho Statesman* identified a prospector named Jamison. Said to have been an old associate of miner Elias D. Pierce who, a decade before, had ignited the Clearwater gold rush, Jamison panned the Snake River's mouth. Working east, he found profitable placer deposits near the mouth of the Bruneau River. Farther east, the deposits increased. A placer bar near Shoshone Falls yielded gold "as high as $40 to the hand."

Placer miner with rocker from *Century Magazine*, 1883. Right: loading a sluice box.

As the high water declined in the late spring and summer of 1870, hundreds and eventually thousands rushed the Snake River placer deposits, prospecting from Hagerman to

Clark's Ferry along a sixty-mile stretch. A camp named Shoshone rose a mile below the Twin Falls. Another called Drytown sat at the mouth of Dry Creek near present-day Murtaugh. Springtown, a third camp located a half mile west of the future site of the Hansen bridge, became the "metropolis of the river," the largest and most important settlement after the Chinese entered the canyon in 1871.

Unlike the gold in California and northern Idaho, which was often found as nuggets, the Snake River gold was very fine placer gold. Placer deposits of sand and gravel contain free or alluvial gold that has eroded out of bedrock veins or lodes, often in association with magnetic "black sands" containing high concentrations of iron oxide. Snake River gold originated in lode deposits near Yellowstone National Park. The Green River in Utah, which has its source in the same area, contains similar fine gold. To the miners trying to recover these minute particles, the gold flakes seemed like flour. During the recovery process, if the volume of water in the sluice or rocker was too forceful, the flour gold could float away. Mining engineer Thomas Egleston described the frustration experienced by a Snake River miner attempting to pan flour gold: "The heavier pieces of the black sand and flour gold remain persistently together. ... After the heavy black sand has been separated by the magnet, the fine particles of gold float. ... When, after much trouble, the surfaces are wetted and the gold is got under the water and onto the top of the sand, the first wave from the other side of the pan over the sand floats the gold again."

The gold appeared to be present in amounts that encouraged prospecting, but a typical ten-acre placer claim miners thought would pay $8 per day would in reality pay only $3.

The gold was "so fine and light," the *Statesman* reported, "that a miner is easily deceived." During the 1870s, when gold fluctuated near $20 an ounce, a Snake River miner needed at least 1,000 colors or flour "particles" to equal one cent.

At Springtown, Shoshone Falls, and Salmon Falls, placer miners relied on rockers and sluices. They preferred working bars exposed by low water, as well as "skim bars" and "bench gravels" deposited right at or just above the high-water line. There were "bench placers" among boulders and gravel in elevated bars as high as one hundred feet above the Snake. At Bell Rapids and between the Upper and Lower Salmon Falls, the gold was erratically scattered in deposits rich enough to entice but mostly too covered with sand and gravel to mine profitably. New hydraulic and ground sluicing methods—filters made from burlap sacks, for example—recovered some additional gold. The richest Snake River deposits were located on Bonanza Bar west of American Falls and from Raft River to Salmon Falls. Miners worked these sites extensively from the 1870s well into the 1900s. Many of the claims along the Snake River were reopened when the Great Depression of the 1930s raised the price of gold from $20 to $35 an ounce.

The miners faced near-impossible hardships in spring and early summer when snowmelt flooded the Snake. Dispatches and letters published in the Boise, Silver City, and Corrinne, Utah, newspapers expressed both the miners' praise and condemnation for the Snake's "vast and singular defile." One miner's angry complaint appeared in *The Idaho Statesman:* "For rattlesnakes, scorpions, mosquitoes, gnats, sagebrush and hot sand it is the

Hard-luck miner Fred Turner at Pierce, Idaho. Left: panning, a tedious method of separating gold flakes from black sand.

best country I have ever seen; but as for gold and a mining country, I cannot say as much, although there is scarcely a place on the river that a man cannot get a prospect, but not in sufficient quantity to pay." Four others found time to play while waiting for placer season. Building "a very fine yacht" and sailing four to eight miles upriver, they marveled at "splendor almost indescribable," at chasms "more formidable than walls surrounding ancient cities. The clear water gushing from the high banks forms falls along the north side, at the foot of which are great resorts for mountain trout."

Chinese miner uses a rocker on placer deposits. Right: evidence of nineteenth-century Chinese mining include a tea box, Tiger Whiskey bottle, coin, and transcript of a deed found in a baking soda can below Twin Falls.

In the spring of 1870, as the season got under way, perhaps 400 to 500 miners persevered in crude encampments. The biggest settlements rose in the area around the Shoshone and Twin Falls. Gold deposits were especially large, reported the *Statesman,* "where the water is very swift and forms eddies, and by the reaction, deposits the precious metal on its banks. Several of these canyons are located near this vicinity [Shoshone Falls], one above here and one below Salmon Falls." Supplies came from the Union Pacific depot at Kelton, Utah, via the Kelton Road that connected Salt Lake City with Boise. The Rock Creek Trading Post, five miles south of Hansen and about nine miles south of the canyon, was the area's only store. Downstream claims at Salmon Falls were far removed from trading centers until Len Lewis, in 1873, took over Payne's Ferry where Kelton Road crossed into the Hagerman Valley about two miles above Thousand Springs.

The first Snake River gold rush was short-lived. Daunted and discouraged by the end of the 1870 season, many miners returned to Boise, Corinne, and Silver City. An item from Silver City's *Owyhee Avalanche* captured the prevailing frustration: "Bob Drummond got back from the Snake River mines this week, and says that he is Snake bitten enough to last him some time."

Chinese miners, first allowed into the canyon in the spring of 1871, bought out the claims abandoned by prospectors too impatient for the frustrating work of sluicing for flour gold. Claims that paid less than three dollars a day did not profit white miners. Wrote one discouraged prospector: "The Chinese are better adapted to this sort of mining and there is room for 500 of them. Therefore, let them come. They can work in peace."

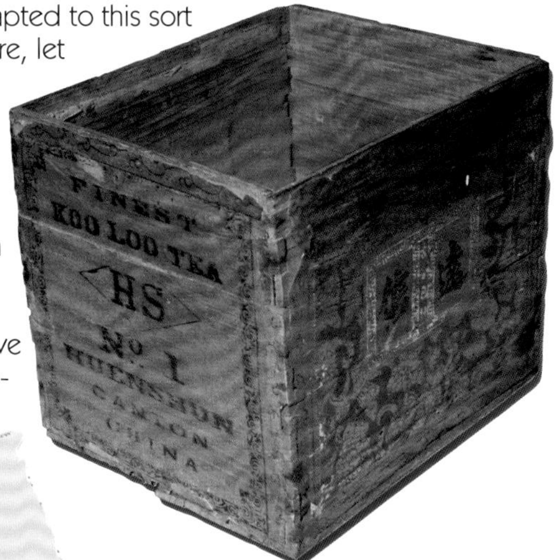

The Chinese invested not only money but also intensive labor, a resource they had in abundance. "Invariably, the Chinese substituted labor for machinery," wrote historian Randall Rohe. In 1857, the *Alta California* reported that "many a claim, abandoned in despair on previous occasions by the impatient American miner, will be made to pay handsome wages by these celestial gold hunters." Labor-intensive mining gave Chinese companies a temporary monopoly in many places.

Archaeological evidence indicates that Chinese miners worked claims throughout the canyons above Salmon Falls. A deed rolled into a can of baking powder—and fortuitously discovered below Twin Falls more than a century after the gold rush—documented the Tung Toek Tong company's November 11, 1871, purchase of Relf Bledsoe's claim at a place

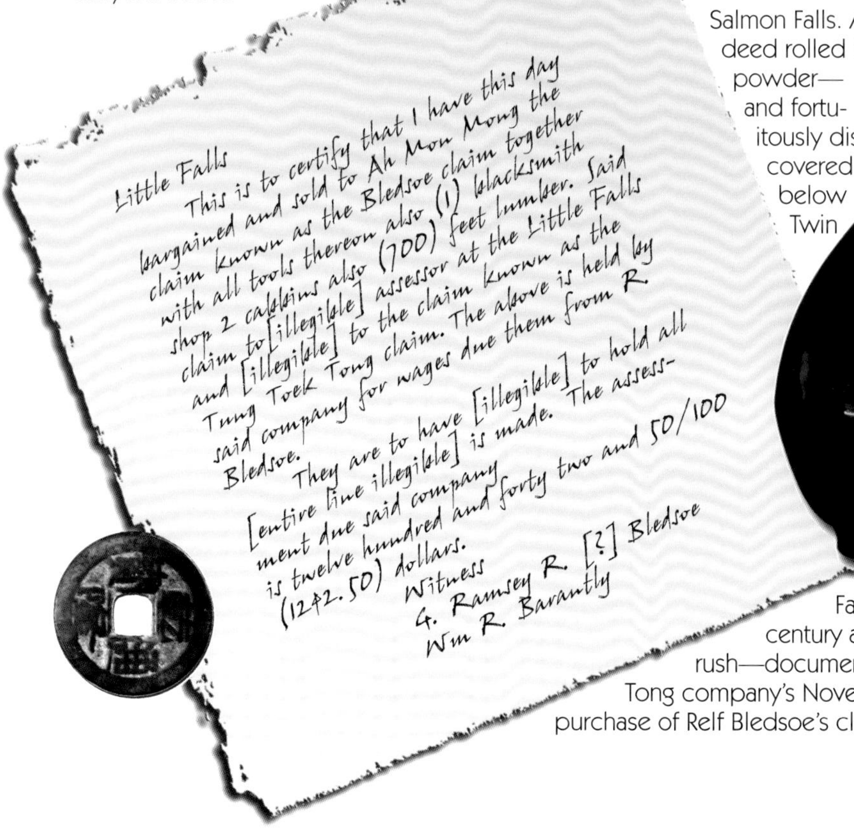

Little Falls
This is to certify that I have this day bargained and sold to Ah Mon Mong the claim known as the Bledsoe claim together with all tools thereon also (1) blacksmith shop 2 cabbins also (700) feet lumber. Said claim to [illegible] assessor at the Little Falls and [illegible] to the claim known as the Tung Toek Tong claim. The above is held by said company for wages due them from R. Bledsoe.
They are to have [illegible] to hold all [entire line illegible] is made. The assessment due said company is twelve hundred and forty two and 50/100 (1242.50) dollars.
[?] Bledsoe
Witness
G. Ramsey R.
Wm R. Barantly

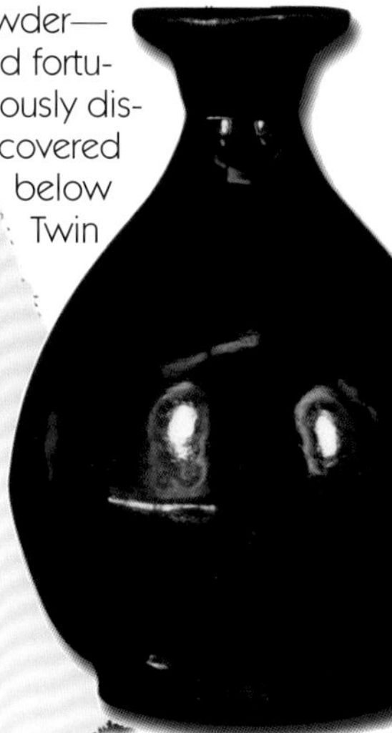

called "Little Falls" (probably Twin Falls). The sale turned the claim over to the Chinese in lieu of wages, implying Bledsoe had employed laborers from the Tung Toek Tong during the sum-

William Doc Hisom, left, and his partner William White worked sluice boxes along the Middle Snake from about 1906 to 1913. Right: Yee-Hi, in suit, sits with an unidentified tough in Blackfoot, Idaho. Inset: an imported opium tin, about 1880. Opium-based patent medicines were common in the gold miners' West.

mer and fall of 1871. Rather than pay the Chinese with gold dust, Bledsoe simply gave them his claim and all the related equipment. Tung Toek Tong most likely referred to one of the fraternal organizations the Chinese formed in those days. The Chinese came to America from Canton on the Pearl River Delta in eastern Guangdong Province near Hong Kong. Most were laborers from villages and farms, but well-educated merchants came too. Their high degree of "business sagacity" helped immensely in the achievement of business success on the American frontier.

A complex network known as the Six Companies connected the Chinese communities scattered across the West with the homeland. The Six Companies was a powerful mercantile organization that represented Chinese from the districts of Guangdong Province. Characterized as clannish, the Cantonese merchants automatically had membership in one of the Six Companies as well as in several tongs. Tongs helped the Chinese preserve their culture in a foreign land, and merchants belonged to at least one clan tong, a secret-society tong for protection, and any number of benevolent tongs. The well-developed mercantile

network of the Six Companies and access to the Snake River placers provided by the Kelton Road made it possible for Chinese miners to maintain contact with Guangdong. Merchants such as Ah Mon Mong, named in the Bledsoe deed, kept the Chinese supplied with a variety of durable and practical items such as ceramic wares and foodstuffs imported from Guangzhou. They also brought in opium.

Smoking opium was once commonplace and perfectly legal in southern China and throughout the gold miners' West. In the 1860s, 1870s, and 1880s, China exported opium packaged in very distinctive rectangular brasslike metal cans containing 6.67 ounces. Trading posts sold it over the counter along with all the other necessities and luxuries such as brandy, tea, gunpowder, and canned goods. Opium-based patent medicines were abundant and widely used, said an advertisement, "to relieve pain and irritation, to relax spasms, to produce sleep, to check secretions, and to influence nutrition." In 1881, the 11th Idaho territorial legislature attempted to discourage the smoking of opium by regulating its sale. Metal opium containers, ceramic pipe bowls, and other kinds of paraphernalia still dot many placer mining archaeological sites.

Chinese coins, or *wen*, with their square holes are another archaeological trace of the gold miners' West. Worthless as currency in camps where gold dust was the medium of exchange, the coins most likely served as gaming pieces or talismans. Perhaps some coins were used for consulting the *I Ching*. Chinese miners also used coins to rub muscles and release the flow of *ch'i* or energy during *Gua Sha*, an ancient folk remedy.

Placer mining waxed and waned with the rise and fall of the Snake and in response to rumors of better claims. By the late 1870s, according to a British tourist, Springtown was merely "a hamlet composed of a few miserable Chinese huts, that lies buried at the base of the canyon 500 feet below. Here I found two merchants who traded with the Chinese miners." Reports of Tom Bell's 1880 ferry disaster were among the last and most sensational stories of the Snake River Chinese. Bell, a fiddle-playing Scottish miner, began a ferry above Shoshone Falls in 1879. Charles Walgamott, who knew Bell, recalled that the miner "was asked to ferry over several Chinamen and their cargo of groceries to the north side. ... All went well until the current was reached, when the Chinamen ashore noticed the boat with its human freight, swirl and plunge bow first towards that awful chasm. Some thought that an oar had been broken, others that the current was just too

The drought-stricken canyon below Hansen Bridge shades the all-but-obliterated ruins of Springtown, an 1870s supply point for the Snake River placer mines. Above: ruins of Desert Station on the Kelton-Boise stage route.

strong. ... It was an exciting scene. All three men in the boat rose to their feet, cries could be heard and one Chinaman was sure Tom Bell sang or chanted. ... In a few seconds all was

Chinese miners work a sluice box, about 1890. Right: detail from a rock wall, evidence of Chinese mining near Springtown.

over, not even a piece of the broken boat was distinguishable from the other drift below the falls. The Chinamen ashore immediately established a camp below the falls to wait for the bodies to rise and as they were recovered they were taken to the top and buried until they could be shipped to China." One of the victims may have been Mon Chu, who, according to Lucy Stricker of Rock Creek Station, was "the leader of the Chinese in the area." Edward Roberts's *Shoshone and Other Western Wonders* mentioned the accident and added that "one or two Chinamen have since shared Bell's fate."

As Chinese left the Snake River in the late 1870s, Euramerican interest revived. In 1875, Johnny Stewart staked a claim known as Mud Creek Bar at the mouth of Mud Creek, near Kanaka Rapids northwest of Buhl. After murdering two employees, Stewart fled to the Black Hills of South Dakota where Souix Indians killed him in turn. Two miners, Andy Brown and Sid Smith, had placer claims along Billingsley Creek that "proved quite profitable." An old hermit named Jimmie Divilbiss built a cabin on a Snake River claim and kept burros to pack in his supplies. One day neighbors found Divilbiss dead in his bunk. Sixty dollars stashed in a can uncovered from the hermit's cabin helped pay for a decent burial in the local cemetery. Partners Will Justice and R.C. Smith, meanwhile, filed on a placer claim in the Salmon Falls district. According to one source, Justice recovered enough flour gold to mint forty $20 gold pieces. In May 1879, Sampsom Reed told *The Idaho Statesman* that "claims adjoining his [near Malad] are making one hundred dollars per twenty-four hours for each claim, working only one man at a time. All that is needed is real work."

The placer revival brought new techniques and more expensive equipment to the Snake River canyons in 1879. Burlap sluices now connected systems of ditches and flumes. Towering as high as seventy feet above the river, the flume-sluice networks flushed ledges and bench deposits. Increasingly the expense of these flume operations required corporate backing—at Salmon Falls and Dolman Island, for example, where the New York Mining Company worked placer deposits. Nearby at Birch Creek in the Hagerman Valley, the California Bar Mining Company planned an elaborate system of ditches and pipes.

Irrigation seepage through unlined canals fed springs that returned to the Snake through the south wall of the canyon near Hansen. Above: Bruneau jasper, found only in the southcentral Idaho canyon lands.

Mining tied Idaho to a global economy in which heavily capitalized corporations depended evermore on flumes, pipes, ditches, and dams. Already in the 1890s an infrastructure invented for gold had seeded pioneer dreams of a wet and pastoral heartland. The homesteader's task was to forge those dreams into tangible plans.

The Homesteaders

The range above those placers was gnarled with greasewood and sage when Lincoln and the Republican Congress made good a campaign promise of "free land to the homeless" with the Homestead Act of 1862. Already the Oregon-bound could follow the Kelton Road to Payne's Ferry at Fishing Falls and west to a wooden-plank stage station that grew into an outpost with a post office and general store. The settlement that would become Hagerman commanded a valley of melon boulders. Temperatures ranged from subzero to 100°F. Winds were so steady and fierce that the people of the Hagerman Valley, even now, call their state "Idablow."

The valley before irrigation typified the semiarid Great Basin with its green-gray cover of Wyoming big sagebrush, spiny hopsage, rabbit brush, and bitter brush. Juniper, willow, and black cottonwood lined cold streams in desert canyons. Rodents proliferated as hunting and grazing drove off the elk and other big game. Mice, rabbits, and ground squirrels lured hawks and golden eagles. Rattlesnakes thrived. So did toads, frogs, songbirds, waterfowl, and upland game birds such as sage grouse and quail. Diverse populations of insects fed abundant fish that were feasted on, in turn, by herons, kingfishers, and white pelicans. Homesteaders, however, were few until cattle filled the desert in the wake of the mining boom.

Cattleman Elmer Cook's relatives ranched the only known homestead on the west side of the Snake River on the site now preserved as the Hagerman Fossil Beds. Born in 1887 in Glenwood, Utah, Cook was orphaned one month after reaching the Hagerman Valley. His grandfather had

been an immigrant from Germany, where the family name was Koch. His father, Wil, had worked gold mines in California and Utah before traveling to Idaho, but little is known of his mother except that she died in Utah when the boy was eight. Returning to Idaho by train at age thirteen after a season of lead mining in Eureka, Utah, Cook attended school, shoveled

coal, and worked as the night bellhop at the McFall Hotel in Shoshone City. He also ran his own cattle and freighted for rancher and future father-in-law John Schooler.

Elmer's son, Dick Cook, and his neighbor Asahel Gridley, in tape-recorded conversations with National Park Service ranger Bob Willhite, pieced together their recollections in a history of those wandering times. Cook said:

"My father Elmer started running cattle here in 1903 as an orphan boy. He went into Charlie Gridley's bank to borrow some money to run cattle on the west side of the river. 'Kid,' Charlie asked, 'Where are your parents?' My father told him that they were dead and that he had been on his own for two years already. Charlie loaned him the money to buy cattle even though he was running them on the same ground that Charlie grazed his horses!"

Asked if the stockmen ever took a break from work during the heat of the day, Asahel Gridley responded, "You're talking about the people that growed up in this country. The goddamn weather didn't bother nobody here. That was just part of living. They never cared what it was." Cook added:

"My dad had some tough times early on, but he was able to buy ten acres and eventually increased it to forty. He did a lot of fishing and looked for arrowheads. Oh, he liked to hunt. Times was too hard to travel. My folks went to the mountains with teams and wagons and stayed some in the summertime. We ran about two hundred head of cattle on the west side of the river; it was good range. My dad and I ran cattle there into the 60s, when the irrigation pumping took over. It was a great, carefree life with lots of work and damned little money. I look back and I think my experiences were worth more than the highest paid job."

Amanda Gooding, wife of Governor Frank Gooding and Idaho's first lady from 1901 to 1905. Previous: a turkey farm near Buhl; a timber-notched cabin on the Shoshone-Paiute Duck Valley reservation; a postage stamp commemorating the 1862 Homestead Act.

Dick Cook still lives on the family ranch in the twilit shadows of the fossil quarries. A collector of cowboy artifacts—diaries, wagons, rodeo buckles, Charley Russell drawings, a miniature windmill, a fire-blackened cast-iron pot that his own people hauled west on the Oregon Trail—Cook can follow the family back five generations on his mother's side:

"My mother's name was Lydia Ann Schooler. Her great-granddad was born in 1813. Her granddad was born in 1842. He came west in 1858, I believe with the Iowa Regiment. They got snowed in at La Grande, Oregon, and almost starved to death there one winter; he wasn't married then—he was fairly young. He went back and got married. They crossed the plains in a wagon in 1862 and come to Fort Boise. Two kids died eating grain, one a Schooler. Don't know who the other boy was. They was basically freighters. They freighted the first lumber into Boise to build the first lumber building. They also freighted the first grain-thrashing machine into Boise. They left there and went to Texas for awhile. When they returned here they settled on the Gridley Island. Then they freighted from Kelton, Utah, to Boise before the railroad come. They went from there up to Wood River and came back to Hagerman about 1890. Then they freighted from Gooding to Wendell and Bliss to Hagerman. They also broke horses and cowboyed—anything they could to make a living. The Schooler Hotel was eventually built in Hagerman. Mom was born in 1894. She was very short and only weighed about 98 pounds. Didn't really talk that much—unless she was mad. She had quite a temper. It took quite a bit to rile her up, though. Oh, she was a hard worker. I can say that for her. Took good care of her family. She liked to cook. She canned quite a lot of fruit and she sewed some, not a great deal. Had a treadle sewing machine and washed on a board."

Dick Cook holds a portrait of great-grandfather William Schooler, who freighted the Kelton Road that paralleled stretches of the Oregon Trail.

Asked if his parents were strict, Cook replied, "Yeah, in a way they were and in another way they weren't. I didn't have any kids to play with, you know. I played alone, but took real good care of my stuff. I've still got what few toys I had. But I'm real sure that if they had ever caught me stealing anything or told a lie they'd have killed me. I know they would've."

Rancher Charlie Gridley, a successful rancher and banker by 1903, had been one of the first settlers to capture and breed some of the thousands of feral horses that a century or two before fled north to the sage plateau. Asahel Gridley said his grandfather Charlie released a herd from California that went wild on the Snake River Plain. "He [grandfather Charlie Gridley] had a lot of wild horses on the desert. I was busy with them most of the time—helping them out with the wild horses. We had about ten thousand of them over the years." According to Cook:

"The Gridleys had a large range horse operation on the west side of the river that started near Glenns Ferry and ran to Three Creek. I saw with my own eyes twenty-five hundred head in the stockyards at Bliss about 1935. You could see dust coming on a horse trail, mostly about sundown. A line of horses would be in a slow trot, maybe a hundred head in a bunch. They would range out a good fifteen miles from water so they did a lot of traveling in a day."

Asahel's father, Frank, was "kinda quiet." Mother Jamie was "a wonderful woman" who rode sidesaddle and straight saddle. She had six children, including a son who died as an infant. The family constructed a rock and

The Union Pacific Railroad's Oregon Short Line reached Shoshone in 1883, Gooding and Glenns Ferry in 1884. Branching north and south to Oakley, Declo, Ketchum, Hill City, and Wells (Nevada), rails opened rich international markets for Idaho livestock and crops. Pictured: Glenns Ferry with its eating house and stock yards become an Oregon Short Line divisional headquarters. Right: terra-cotta detail from the U.P.'s Shoshone depot; an Oregon Short Line timetable, about 1900.

pole corral adjacent to Tuana Springs a few miles northwest of the fossil beds. Cook remembered that the springs were "just a trickle" yet enough to water the horses. Almost a century

30 MINUTES HUNT

BISBEE PHOTO.
318

later, Cook showed a park service archaeologist the remains of a larger wood post and wire corral west of Hagerman. "People would come over and watch us brand," said Gridley, recalling the one hundred-by 150-foot heavy gauge wire corral. Cook added:

"There were a lot of branding irons out there. Some of those young kids wanted to ride a colt. They'd jump right on 'em. Buck like hell! People would come over and pick horses they wanted right out of the corral. We'd halter break them and take them across the river whenever they wanted them. We didn't get much out of them; everybody got a horse if they wanted one."

Rabbit hunting became a ritualized sport in which entire communities turned out to beat the sagebrush and drive the jacks into V-shaped pens. Left: a Snake River homestead. Following: making hay, about 1900. A derrick from the heyday of ditch irrigation looms over a scattering of inventive contraptions at a farm museum south of Jerome.

Because animals full of water were easier to herd, the Gridleys would hold horses off for a day then let them drink their fill. Cook explained:

"They had a pole corral on a ridge flat with a long wire netting wing running downhill towards the river. On the wing they tied white rags all over it so the horses could see it even when it was dark. They'd herd 'em right in. I remember one time we rode up to the corral when Gridleys were working colts; someone wanted to know if I wanted something to eat. Sure, I said! There was a branding fire with a lot of colt fries [testicles of gelded colts] roasting in it. I was only about six years old so they thought colt fries would turn my stomach, but the joke was on them. I ate them and wanted more. I had eaten hundreds of fries by then."

Jailhouse celebrity Jack "Diamond Field" Davis. After a U.S. Supreme Court hearing, eight stays of execution, five years behind bars in Cassia County and a sixth in the Idaho State Penitentiary, state officials pardoned the flamboyant gunman of the 1896 murder of two Rogerson-area sheepherders. Anger over the pardon fueled the pro-sheep gubernatorial bid of Lincoln County Republican Frank Gooding, elected in 1904. Below: Front page of the Idaho *Daily Statesman*, April 17, 1897.

After branding, the Gridleys swam a few range horses across the river below the corral. Explained Cook:

"We swam our saddle horses there back of a boat, usually three or four at a time. I saw a few horses drown. If they give up and get their head under, that is it. We swam a lot of cows there but a cow won't drown; they float. Gridleys branded with a CG and in later years a box on one side of the jaw, then a box on both jaws. We branded with a pitchfork on the right ribs of our cattle."

Branded horses were sold at the rail yards. "Took 1,500 off [to market] the first year," said Gridley. "Got six bucks a head for 'em at Bliss. They shipped them out of there for meat."

Once, Gridley continued, "a posse came across my dad workin' horses. He had a hell of a time convincin' those S.O.B.'s that he wasn't a robber. My dad was a good shot, but they didn't lose anybody." Cook expanded on the story:

"Two teenage boys robbed a hardware store in Wendell and stole a few things including some

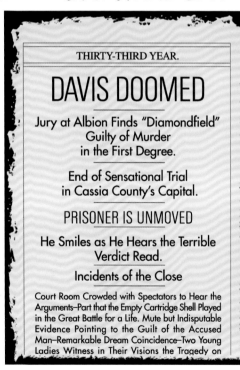

THIRTY-THIRD YEAR.

DAVIS DOOMED

Jury at Albion Finds "Diamondfield" Guilty of Murder in the First Degree.

End of Sensational Trial in Cassia County's Capital.

PRISONER IS UNMOVED

He Smiles as He Hears the Terrible Verdict Read.

Incidents of the Close

Court Room Crowded with Spectators to Hear the Arguments–Part that the Empty Cartridge Shell Played in the Great Battle for a Life. Mute but Indisputable Evidence Pointing to the Guilt of the Accused Man–Remarkable Dream Coincidence–Two Young Ladies Witness in Their Visions the Tragedy on

guns. The two boys came down to the Owsley Ferry and crossed to the west side of the river. In the meantime, Wendell organized a posse to hunt down the two boys; they were well armed and mounted on horses. The posse split into two groups on the west side of the river to cover more country. Each group rode around each side of a small hill in a fast lope. When they met, panic took over and they began to shoot at each other. Lucky there wasn't a good shot in the bunch so no one was hurt. Next they went to the bottom of

Yahoo Canyon where Gridleys had a horse camp, opened fire, and ran all of them into the brush. They didn't hurt anyone at that camp, but later on they ran into the two boys and shot and killed one of them. By this time the people of Hagerman had had enough of Wendell's posse so they got together a posse of their own and went after Wendell's posse. They found them headed back to Wendell with the boy's body in a wagon. Hagerman's posse told them not to say or do one more thing wrong or they would shoot all of them. I guess they made a real quiet trip being escorted by Hagerman's posse all the way back to Wendell."

Though Gridley recalled only one Indian—WWI-veteran Buck Nelson who lived on one of the islands—the valley remained wild enough for the

Young cowboy, Twin Falls, about 1908. Below: Buhl, Idaho, platted in 1905 and named for Frank H. Buhl, financier of the Twin Falls canal. Left: steam-powered tractors freighted supplies to the Hollister area, about 1910.

first generation of homesteaders on the desert near Wendell and Bliss. "There was a steep sandy bank just before the trail reached the top that was hard for me to climb," Cook remembered.

"Unbeknownst to me I had cornered a large rattlesnake against the bank that could not get away. He was getting ready to fight. I didn't see the snake but my father who was back of me did; he let out a yell that would have put a steam whistle to shame. He then grabbed me by the arm and threw me down the bluff. I must have sailed a good fifteen feet landing on my face with my mouth full of sand. It scared the hell right out of me but it was better than being bit by a rattlesnake. My mother was mad as hell at my father for throwing me so far, but he was excited."

Gridley also commented about snakes: "Pretty near everyday I passed rattlesnakes going up there. In those days there were lots of rattlesnakes; there was lots of bitter brush." Most of the farming back then was on the Hagerman side of the river where pioneer irrigators had converted the placer canals. Below the fossil bluffs on the monument side the sandy terrain defeated irriga-

tion until the 1920s when settler Fred Conklin contrived an ingenious way to ferry creek water across the river with a cable-suspended pipe. "Fred Conklin was my mother's uncle," Cook explained. Conklin's pipeline tapped water that ran through the flat where Lydia Schooler was born. There on the east (Hagerman) side of the river the Schoolers had a dugout cabin. Cook continued:

"Early people here would just kind of dig a hole in the side of a hill and put a roof over it. Fred [Conklin] built a shack on that flat. For a few years a man by the name of Lou Day and his wife lived there. Mrs. Day was related to my mother somehow, but I don't recall how. The house exterior was covered with tarpaper, and on a hot day you could smell it a mile away. There was also a root cellar dug into a bank, and up the canyon was a little spring box to get water and keep food cool. A road extended west past the house and up a ridge to the top of the plateau. It was actually a well-traveled horse trail."

Rattlers thrived in the lava desert, especially near Rattlesnake Station above Mountain Home. Left: timber ruins of an 1880s ranch house near Hollister.

Near the site of the future pipeline, Conklin and his neighbors, the Brailsford family, first built a cable ferry. Sheep ferried across the river grazed fresh grass on the east-side bluffs. Asked if cowboys used the ferry, Gridley said, "Nah, we'd just jump the horses into the river." Irrigation, however, benefited farmers and ranchers alike. "My father, Elmer," said Cook, "helped Fred [Conklin] build

the pipeline, which was a large undertaking in those days." The neighbors borrowed a chain block and tackle from Idaho Power Company. "It took a full day to winch the heavy cable

only a few feet. They anchored the cable in good, up in the rocks, not far from the dugout where my mother was born." Two ditches split water from the wooden pipe. One ditch skirted a ridge and ran south about a quarter mile to a small patch of alfalfa. A shorter ditch cut through some placer deposits and went about 200 feet

Straw-roofed dugout potato cellar near Buhl. Left: the characteristic basalt masonry of a Shoshone storefront.

northeast. But the system was never completed. "One winter," Cook explained, "students playing hooky built a fire in the end of the wooden pipe and burned it all down." The fire destroyed the pipe. Cut off from water and broke, Conklin abandoned the homestead. Rabbits ate the alfalfa as grass reclaimed the corral.

No one remembers exactly when Fred and the Conklin clan gave up on the Hagerman homestead. Eventually the ferry sank. Fences collapsed. Sand filled the shanty ditches. Wind and time and neglect dismantled tarpaper shacks. A 1934 photograph shows the ruin of a swinging pipeline—a single broken tripod, an iron ferry cable still sagging into the Snake.

Paradise Reborn

Thomas Gray rode herd in a desert of snakes and badgers in the dawn of the golden era made magic at Milner Dam. A wrangler with a frowning mustache—broad hat, buttoned vest, silk scarf, silver spurs looped to his sharp-toed boots in the style of the Idaho cowboy—Gray, in 1902, was Nebraska-bound near Kelton with 400 Idaho horses when a Central Pacific train spooked and ran off the herd. "The engine," Gray recalled, "came around the curve and whistled. The whole herd came back against me. I had to out run them for about half a mile with the leaders tromping on my horse's heels." The stampede hit a barbed wire fence and raced through tall alfalfa. "I could see hay shocks rising 20 feet high," wrote Gray. Passing trains kept the stampede running. Gray, his herd crippled and scattered, lost forty-two horses in all.

Gray dodged fences and trains on Idaho's middle landscape. A geography first explored by historian Leo Marx in *The Machine in the Garden: Technology and the Pastoral Ideal in America*, it sat in the middle between ranching and modernization where Middle Snake civilization wrangled with two ideals. One ideal, always, was efficiency through engineering—the machine. Another was escape to a tranquil heartland of ranches and farms—the garden. Idaho pioneers felt compelled to dominate wild country, yet they pined for a simpler, greener, more chaste and pastoral America. They turned to nature for inspiration without wanting to return there on a permanent basis. They fretted about modernization without losing faith in tools and machines. Technology—a sacrament, a panacea, a high expression of agrarian virtue in Gray's America—would regenerate the farming republic according to God's masterful plan. "God, a sort of Chief Engineer, had drawn up the blueprints and built the framework," historian Mark Fiege explained in *Irrigated Eden: The Making of an Agricultural Landscape in the American West*, his excellent book about Snake River irrigation. Technology alone was no match for a lava desert. Eden came only to those who respected nature enough to develop the creeks and draws where water naturally drained.

In Idaho the dream of industrial Eden rose like a watery phoenix in spiritual and secular forms. Under the leadership of Thomas Ricks, a Mormon bishop and delegate to the National Irrigation Congress, the Great Feeder Dam supplied the world's most sprawling network of gravity canals. Built on the South Fork of the Snake near Rexburg in 1894–95, the dam showcased what could be done by church guidance and family labor. Five years later another church-sponsored project used timber and rock and the same

Cattleman James "Buck" Buchanan Rice, an 1879 emigrant from Missouri, built a rock cabin and later a plank house with a root cellar in the Stricker ranching district near Rock Creek. Rice ran cattle along Salmon Falls Creek and into the Hagerman Valley. His dairy products reached Ketchum, sustaining the Wood River mines.

kind of family labor to impound the mainstream Snake above Idaho Falls.

Mormons saw the land as a province of Zion. Intensely materialistic yet communitarian and anticapitalist, they repudiated the factory city, embracing instead a bucolic Canaan reborn through sophisticated engineering. Their gospel found secular words in a federal program for free-enterprise reclamation called the Carey Act of 1894. Boosted by entrepreneurs or "silk-hatters," the Carey Act resembled federal aid to the railroads: land grants of up to a million acres for construction too monumental to be financed by states or the farmers themselves. Silk-hatters made a distinction between "rainfall farming" and the precise agricultural "science" that reduced reclamation to a series of standardized steps. Rainfall farming was gamble and guesswork.

Science allowed the Idaho farmer to "laugh at the cloudless skies" because "the much needed moisture [was] under perfect control."

Where rocky and marginal land sank traditional farming, this gospel was especially strong. Engineer E.

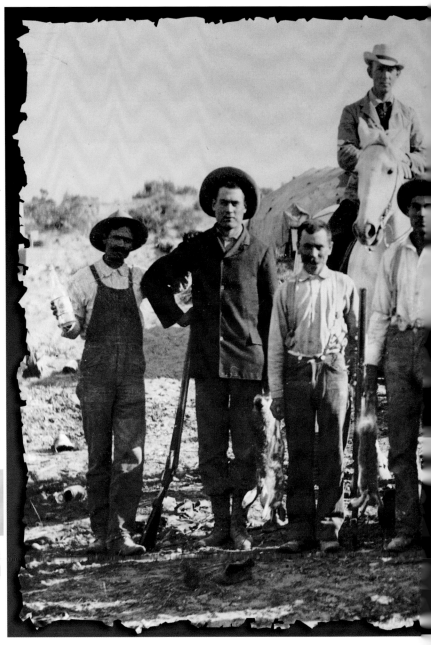

Italian canal workers at a tent city near Murtaugh, 1905.

B. Darlington saw canal construction in Jerome County as the seed of an industrial hub. "There will be better transportation facilities and therefore better markets," wrote Darlington in 1920. North-side irrigation would bring "great indus-

trial plants, such as sugar factories, cheese factories, creameries, ice plants, dehydrating plants, flour mills, alfalfa meal mills, canning factories, great elevators, and warehouses. Train loads of cattle, sheep, wool and farm produce will roll out, and returns will role in." Silk-hatters had already raised more than one hundred million out-of-state dollars for at least twenty-five major projects. Southern Idaho had become, said the *Denver Post*, "The Land of Opportunity." Even the long-detested *Artemisia tridentata*, the desert sagebrush, now symbolized bountiful nature. In 1911, in the China Creek highlands of Twin Falls County, a soil scientist found "a healthy growth of sagebrush." One monstrous plant stood a foot taller than a man on horseback. "This is extra-ordinary," the expert reported. "Both scientists and laymen agree that sagebrush growth is an index of the general character of the land."

Thomas Gray, the wrangler, caught a glimpse of the transformation on his return trip from Nebraska. Traveling by train to Shoshone Depot and then by stage to Rock Creek Station, Gray stopped for supper in a canyon oasis where a dairyman from Indiana had built a fine hotel. There on the banks of the Snake was a clover meadow with English sheep. Thousands of trees, all transplanted, heavy with prize-winning fruit.

A rare turn-of-the-century grain silo built by German American farmers near Buhl. Right: stacking sacks of seed with a conveyor in a Twin Falls warehouse.

The farmer was Ira Burton Perrine, a visionary. Modest and balding and physically small, Perrine had colossal plans for a gleaming city sustained by Carey Act reclamation. Already the farmer had partnered with Salt Lake banker Stanley Milner, Pennsylvania industrialist Frank Buhl, Chicago financier Peter Kimberly, civil engineers Walter Filer and Mark Murtaugh, and hydro developer Harry Hollister—all of whom would earn place-names in the future valley. Incorporated in 1900 and reorganized in 1903, the Twin Falls Land and Water Company selected a dam site at the southern-most loop of the Snake where lava islands constricted the channel. A Perrine subsidiary sold lots in a rabbit-infested barren that became, in 1904, the "magic city" named Twin Falls.

At the dam named for Stanley Milner, the excavation began with a ripping blast that killed a workman and threw rocks for almost a mile. Completed in 1905, the dam was a rubble sensation. Concrete piers anchored three great stony embankments with ninety-nine spillway gates. About 500 men and almost an equal number of horses built a nine-mile raised canal to Dry Creek Reservoir, now Murtaugh Lake. On March 1, opening day, a thousand spectators lined the river below the spillway where rumor had it that golden nuggets could be scooped from the empty Snake. Within a year some 15,000 acres had been ditch irrigated. With 130,000 south-side acres under cultivation by 1908, the Twin Falls project, said its promoters, was "the largest and most intricate system of irrigated canals in the world."

By then the city of Twin Falls was a branch stop on the Oregon Short Line. Billed as the Chicago of Idaho, the instant city sprouted two hotels, three banks, nine churches, paved and lighted sidewalks, piped water and modern sewers, a monumental yellow-brick classical revival courthouse, and abundant hydroelectricity from the Perrine-Hollister powerhouse at Shoshone Falls. "Just to think that this entire city has been hauled over the Blue Lakes grade," said Sen. Fred T. Dubois in 1905. "It is wonderful." Twin Falls was "a happy trinity of soil, sunshine, and water, ... a veritable Paradise," said the Chamber of Commerce in 1909.

Twin Falls was also a businessman's city and pridefully white. The black and Hispanic cowboys once common in Twin Falls County made no mark in the city census. Twin Falls boasted a higher percentage of American-born citizens than any western boomtown. The *Twin Falls Weekly News*, reporting on local Greeks in 1909, denounced the immigrants for the un-American practice of hoarding farm wages for families abroad. Five years later two Chinese attempted to lease a restaurant site on Main Street. The Chinese were "invading the city," the *News* reported. A mob soon drove the two out of town. Protestant Twin Falls also discouraged Irish, Italian, and Basque immigrants by prohibiting liquor in Catholic enclaves and punishing saloons with a $2,000 annual tax. Twin Falls, nevertheless, was self-consciously "progressive" and "undoubtedly the most metropolitan, most flourishing and busiest little city of its age and size in the country," said boosters in 1910.

Magic Dam on the Big Wood River set off a land rush to Richfield, a Carey Act township platted in 1908. Right: Peruvian sheepherders on the Camas Prairie have adopted a lonely vocation once dominated by immigrant Basques.

Above Twin Falls the desert buzzed with construction wherever rushing water in vertical canyons brought out-of-state dollars for dams. The U.S. Reclamation Service used 14,000 barrels of concrete and almost a mile of rock to impound the Snake at Minidoka, creating Lake Walcott. Completed in 1906, Minidoka Dam became the centerpiece of a seven-dam project that irrigated more than a million acres through 1,600 miles of canals and nearly 4,000 miles of laterals. The 1909 Minidoka powerhouse with its five great generators pioneered rural electrification. Rupert, a planned city named for its engineer, gained national fame for its brick, three-story, electrically heated high school.

Where the Big Wood River met Camas Creek, meanwhile, the Idaho Irrigation Company used 450 kegs of blasting powder and 500-man crews of mostly immigrant labor to build one of the world's largest earthen dams. Magic Dam, so-called, gave rise to a company town called Richfield, founded in 1908. "The dam is as deep up and down the stream as three city blocks, almost a city block high, and more than two blocks long," according to the *Richfield Recorder*. Some 400 miles of canals and a wood-stave, five-feet diameter pipe forked water to Dietrich and Gooding. Dietrich, a Carey Act land rush town, captured the buoyant mood when a wag blocked out the "t" on the railroad's welcoming sign. "Die rich" the sign now advised. The desert, no longer "hopeless" and

"discouraging," had become "a comparative Paradise," said *Harper's Weekly*. Southcentral Idaho had become "a miracle of modern American life."

The miracle transformed Idaho demographics in ways the boosters expected and ways many did not. Canal construction diversified labor, luring immigrants from Greece, Ireland, Italy, Austria, and Spain. Basque masons and carpenters found welcome escape from the sheep camps on irrigation projects. Polkas and the button accordion came to the Buhl-Castleford area with an influx of Czech-American farmers in 1907. Swedes dotted the eastern desert in an experimental colony named New Sweden and another named Firth. In beet country, however, Amalgamated Sugar preferred low-paid seasonal labor. Wartime demand for potatoes and beets brought stoop labor from Mexico, the Philippines, and India in 1917. Japanese immigrants, many of them railroad workers, joined the Idaho harvest with the hope of raising capital to lease or buy farming lands. In 1921 the Idaho Senate defeated legislation to exclude the Japanese irrigators from owning farmland. Two decades before the U.S. Army confined some 9,500 Japanese Americans at the Minidoka Relocation Center, the "thrifty" Japanese allegedly had "an absolute genius for the reclamation of bad land." Population boomed in the wake of big irrigation. From 3,143 people in 1890, the eight-county census jumped to 77,000 by the end of World War I.

Had all the valley been like Twin Falls, had Jerome County been less porous, had the summer of 1919 not been one of the driest on record, had potato prices stayed buoyant after World War I, then the miracle might have continued. Jerome's north-side system of reservoirs and canals would have prospered had nature truly been "very kind" in providing what Perrine and company called "a system of drainage that cannot be duplicated by man." Hundreds had rushed for land near the town of Jerome as the North Side Canal raced west in 1907. At Big Sugar Loaf Butte, however, a reservoir disappeared through porous strata. A second attempt to hold water in Jerome Reservoir likewise failed. "I had a nice little bunch of money when I came here," wrote a settler from Jerome in 1919, "[but] today I have just 50 cents left." Four out of five Jerome-area settlers had already abandoned their farms.

Perrine Bridge, 475 feet above the Snake River. The 1927 engineering sensation was the world's tallest bridge.

The Carey Act project on Salmon Falls Creek, meanwhile, was an even greater fiasco. Spearheaded by James and William Kuhn of Pittsburgh, the same brothers who financed Jerome, the Twin Falls Salmon River Land and Water Company had raised $2 million from the sale of 73,000 acres before farmers saw through the con. In 1907 the Kuhn engineers planned a $3 million concrete-arch dam with a 180,000 acre-feet reservoir. Shareholders forfeited land as seepage throughout the tract sank the Kuhn corporation. Dutch immigrants had worked five years to develop a parcel called Amsterdam. In 1916, a descendant recalled, "they just walked out." Sagebrush overcame fields more profusely than ever before.

Farmer Perrine, age 82, had built and lost and rebuilt several waterborne fortunes by the time of his death in the Twin Falls Hospital in 1943. "His monument is a rolling carpet of lush vegetation," the *Times-News* reported. His legacy, added *National Geographic*, was "fat bank accounts" and "beautiful homes" and "seven hundred bushels of potatoes to the acres" and "a thousand bushels of sweet Spanish onions" and "enough carrots with their vitamin A to strengthen for night-flying the eyes of all the airmen in the war." Indians defeated, civilization planted, wealth created, savagery subdued—it was a flag-waving tale of seamless progress, of defiant farmers and ranchers who refused to accept nature's terms. Always the tellers of those tales assumed—like Thomas Jefferson, like the frontier historian Frederick Jackson Turner—that settlement meant agriculture, that the snowmelt was virtually boundless and its rush through vertical canyons was a gold mine of national wealth.

Railyard at Gooding. Above: power mower detail from Jerome County's farm museum.

No matter that every action caused a reaction on Idaho's middle landscape. No matter the seepage, the droughts, the cheat, the rodent and insect plagues. "Truly magic it is," said *National Geographic* in a 1944 article that politely ignored migrant workers and the Japanese American "camp" called Minidoka. "In each irrigation-born town old timers told us they remembered when a particularly rich tract belonged to sagebrush." The machine in the garden, it seemed in the 1940s, kept the sun and the windblown soil and the power of water in motion under perfect scientific control.

◆

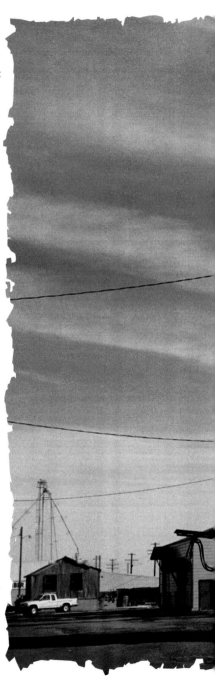

Kathryn Baxter, M.A.
History, Boise State University
Mathew Henbest
History, Boise State University

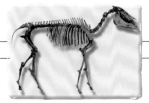
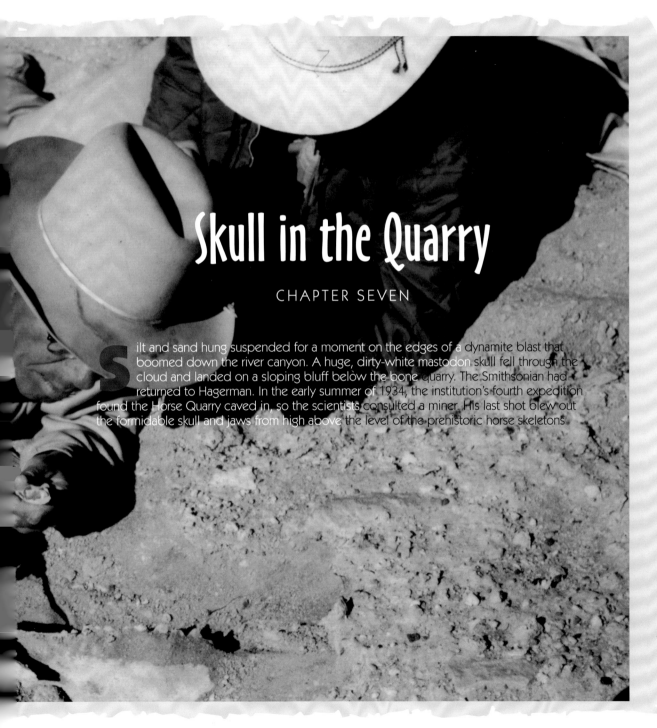

Skull in the Quarry

CHAPTER SEVEN

ilt and sand hung suspended for a moment on the edges of a dynamite blast that boomed down the river canyon. A huge, dirty-white mastodon skull fell through the cloud and landed on a sloping bluff below the bone quarry. The Smithsonian had returned to Hagerman. In the early summer of 1934, the institution's fourth expedition found the Horse Quarry caved in, so the scientists consulted a miner. His last shot blew out the formidable skull and jaws from high above the level of the prehistoric horse skeletons.

that put Hagerman on the scientific map. "We retrieved most of the larger fragments," wrote the Smithsonian's C. Lewis Gazin, "and it is hoped that we may be able to piece some of them together in the laboratory."

Early Idaho had fossil fever. In 1933, C. S. Wheeler of American Falls wrote of bones "very wonderful in appearance, you know they must be at least 3 thousand years old. Some say that have saw the bones they are a giant human, but that is not the question. It is what we

may find in the same place I have found these because it is the most attractive place in nature I have seen in all my travels, it is a bone yard of bygone ages. Still I can not give my fossils away." Mrs. Althea Fouch shared that sentiment. As secretary of the Idaho State Historical Society in 1935, she expressed concern over Gazin's apparently cavalier attitude toward Hagerman's fossils. Claiming the institution had given the impression that nothing of any importance was discovered, Fouch called for laws to "force the large institutions of the east to divide their findings in excavations with the states." This teapot tempest reflected a national investment in all things ancient and wild.

Well-Handled Wilderness

As an infant nation, the United States had faced an identity crisis. With no long history to showcase in great cathedrals and stately museums, America needed its own cultural identity to establish itself beside European nations who looked down their civilized noses at the upstart transplants in the New World. Abbé Raynal wrote from France, "One must be astonished that America has not yet produced one good poet, one able mathematician, one man of genius in a single art or a single science." Thomas Jefferson replied, " ... this reproach is as unjust as it is unkind; and that, of the geniuses which adorn the present age, America contributes its full share." Jefferson noted the contributions of George Washington to liberty, Benjamin Franklin to physics, and David Rittenhouse to astronomy, but something unmistakably American was required for national justification. The new nation would find its pride in wilderness.

Arthur Lake's *Como Bluffs Fieldwork* depicts America's passion for fossil hunting, about 1878. Right: wooly mammoth skeleton from the Smithsonian Natural History Museum. Previous: Claude Hibbard excavates a camel jaw at Hagerman with Jay Larsen, 1967.

Following the Civil War, the tension between using the country's natural resources and preserving them prompted citizens to organize and the federal government to expand its role in the realm of conservation. President Ulysses S. Grant signed the Yellowstone Park Act on March 1, 1872, creating the country's first national park. In 1888, gentleman big-game hunters led by Theodore Roosevelt and George Bird Grinnell, a future president of the National Parks Association, formed the Boone and Crockett Club. The slaughter of birds for the millinery trade had led Grinnell to propose an organization for the protection of wild birds and their eggs, and Audubon societies sprang up throughout the states. But the personal conflict between two wilderness lovers would split the fledgling conservation movement into factions that defined more than a century of activism.

John Muir championed wildness for its own sake. In spite of the harsh work required on the frontier homestead of his boyhood, he regarded civilization as cruel and nature as the means to spiritual fulfillment. Schooled in science and transcendentalism, he developed a

"Everybody needs beauty as well as bread, places to play in and pray in, where nature may heal and give strength to body and soul alike. Brought into right relationships with the wilderness, man would see that his appropriation of Earth's resources beyond his personal needs would only bring imbalance and begat ultimate loss and poverty by all." John Muir, Sierra Club founder.

philosophy focused on the mystical ability of wilderness alone to counteract the oppressive effects of human society. According to Muir, "Why should man value himself as more than a small part of the one great unit of creation?" Gifford Pinchot devoted himself to the management of wilderness. His love of woodlands and fishing led him into a forestry career, but his outdoor experience resulted in a more utilitarian approach to natural wealth. Schooled in Europe's timberlands, where trees were treated as a crop, he developed a philosophy focused on the ability of civilization to provide national well-being through the development of natural resources. According to Pinchot, "A well-handled farm gets more and more productive as the years pass. So does a well-handled forest."

In the summer of 1896, the bearded Muir and the moustached Pinchot met in Montana during a Forestry Commission woodlands tour. Their mutual enthusiasm for forests initially drew them together, but that fall the commission split over its policy recommendations for the management of the forest reserves. Muir's group wanted more forests preserved from commercial use, and Pinchot's group wanted forest reserves opened for economic development. Muir understood the validity of both claims on the environment. Even as founding member and president of the Sierra Club—organized in 1892 specifically for wilderness preservation—he tried to accommodate progress, praising Pinchot's "wise management" model. Compromise proved impossible, however, and the two men broke in 1897 over the issue of grazing sheep in forest reserves. While Muir shifted his efforts to fostering national parks, Pinchot organized the United States Forest Service. By the early 1900s, Pinchot and his colleagues had made wise use synonymous with conservation, but Muir's wilderness proponents enjoyed unprecedented grassroots support. When the Smithsonian Institution ventured to Hagerman at the end of the Roaring Twenties to uncover fossils at a future national monument site, conservation had become part of the American social environment, and wilderness had become a cult.

Rattlesnakes & Scorpions

Hagerman sits directly opposite a series of steep bluffs shaped by the Snake River cutting through the sand, silt, and clay sediments of the Glenns Ferry Formation. Fossils accumulated here over three million years ago on what is now a plateau west of the river. Only 14,500 years ago, the Bonneville Flood's enormous deluge ripped across the plain and covered the valley floor, leaving behind the rounded basalt boulders, called melon gravels, that litter the country-side. Through millennia, runoff from seasonal rains deeply dissected the flood-carved bluffs and created ravines that exposed fossils—a treasury of fossils including the world's largest sample of the extinct zebralike ancestor to all modern horses.

In the early 1920s, Hagerman rancher Elmer Cook discovered the future site while chasing cows in an inaccessible wash on the west side of the Snake River. He began col-lecting a large cache of fossils, sometimes dumping out his Bull Durham to save the small bones of mice, shrews, or fish in the tobacco sack. Cook wrote letters for several years trying to interest the government in his find, but the bones did not gain national attention until 1928 when Harold Stearns of the U.S. Geological Survey found fossils on Cook's front porch. Gathering data on Idaho ground-water resources, the geologist had heard about the rancher's large collection and paid him a visit. Impressed with Cook's bones, Stearns asked to see the site and collect fos-sils of his own. He sent almost 200 pounds of material to Dr. James Gidley at the Smithsonian's National Museum. He identified the bones as a fossilized horse species and wasted no time arranging the first of four Smithsonian excavations over the next six years.

"Cultural and natural resources are the fabric of our heritage—they define our communities, our regions, and our nation. More than icons, they are resources we hold in public trust for future gener-ations. Our American lifestyles depend on the health and vitality of these irreplaceable assets." Neil King, Hagerman Fossil Beds National Monument superintendent.

Gidley left Washington on June 24, 1929, for Idaho Falls to meet Stearns. He spent the days following his arrival surveying major areas of southern Idaho, including McCammon, American Falls, Twin Falls, and Bliss. After thoroughly exploring the countryside, Gidley, Stearns, C. P. Singleton, Fred Conklin, Elmer Cook, and Frank Garnier made camp on the plateau above what would later be named the Hagerman Horse Quarry. The Smithsonian had persuaded Singleton, credited with the discovery of the important Pleistocene fossil locality in Melbourne, Florida, to come west and be part of possibly another grand discovery. Gidley hired Hagerman local Conklin to construct boxes for shipping the fragile fossils back to the National Museum in Washington, D.C. Cook pulled himself away from his ranch to dig in the quarry and prospect other areas. His enthusiasm and knowledge of the area made him a valuable asset on all four Smithsonian digs. Gidley also hired Garnier, another local resident, as the cook and camp man. When Garnier left the dig at the end of July, Idaho Power Company had employed most of the available men in the region to erect a new power plant. Finding a replacement proved difficult until Cook's wife, Lydia Ann, agreed to keep the camp in order and prepare the meals.

The expedition members planned to acquire good collections of fossil bones from the

more important localities and determine the age of the various sedimentary deposits of the Snake River Valley. Material gathered during the trip would be used for exchange with other museums, as well as for study and exhibition at the National Museum. By early July, Assistant Secretary of the Smithsonian Alexander Wetmore decided Gidley's work should focus on Idaho for

the rest of the summer of 1929. In his July 9 letter to Gidley, Wetmore suggested a postponement of the planned expedition to Montana in favor of additional time in the Magic Valley. On July 21, Gidley responded: "I agree with you that the Idaho work is now of major importance the rest being side issues to be postponed or abandoned as seems best later, and of course Hagerman is at present the chief point of attack." He had already shipped 1,300 pounds of horse fossils to the Smithsonian, and he hinted there might be enough material in the "old hill" to supply all the big museums of the country with exceptional collections.

In August, fossil bones still came strong. The group had

Paleontologist Edward Drinker Cope, who discovered the first fragment of *Equus simplicidens* in the early 1890s, theorized in Cope's Rule that species tend to grow ever larger as they evolve. Left: the Snake River cuts the fossil-filled canyons near Hagerman in Idaho artist Archie B. Teater's *Mountain River*.

already prepared four boxes for shipment to Washington, while nearly five more waited for storage. Abundant and easy to dig, some of the fossils proved hard for the Smithsonian staff to handle. Blocks of bones in plaster casts could weigh several hundred pounds and required a wooden sled to remove. Four men in single file pulled a nailed-together contraption of tent ridgepoles and two-by-fours up the steep trail a quarter mile to camp. Later, since the trail was too narrow for a horse team, they used Cook's old workhorse, Fred. Gidley explained in a letter the difficulty of salvaging the delicate fossils: "They are in soft sand, many of them partly encased in a hard contemporary rock, and usually mixed without rhyme or reason. To add to our troubles many of the bones not protected by the rock are very fragile and much cracked up requiring much gum and plaster, then even it is not possible to save some of them."

Preserving the brittle bones was only one kind of trouble for the crew; Snake River scor-

A Smithsonian dig in the early 1930s unearthed a horse skull and skeleton from the ancient riverbed that runs deep into the Horse Quarry's hill. Right: fossil hunters dig through Hagerman's fragile volcanic ash and river sand sediments.

pions and rattlesnakes provided another. The Smithsonian determined that a nine-inch scorpion captured by Cook on the Hagerman bluffs was one of the world's largest. A week later he found another eleven inches long. He put the scorpion in a tomato can and tried to carry it out in his pack, but when he heard it prying at the lid, he let it go. Once Cook had to grab his young son, Dick, and throw him down the hill when the boy cornered a rattlesnake on the narrow, steep-sided trail to the quarry. While snakes and scorpions startled, the weather aggravated. In nearly every letter Gidley wrote, he mentioned the heat or the wind and sometimes both. The intense heat prompted early morning starts, and the high winds meant work might be delayed or called off for the day. Some of the men had to have a doctor probe wind-blown sand from their ears. Water especially was a tough issue for the camp. Their nearest source, the Snake River, required negotiating a steep slope with a horse carrying the five-gallon milk cans used for storage. In the cool mornings, the water tasted delicious. By evening, "the liquid would boil eggs and nobody cared whether they drank it or not." Gidley even refused to let the tobacco-chewing Garnier share the communal canvas waterbag.

Though strict about water and work, Gidley was good-natured. When the crew inadvertently got into an ant nest, he danced around and stripped off with the rest of them. Singleton, a pipe-smoking Georgian in jodhpurs, laughed at others' ant bites but had to endure his own torment when the snake skeleton he claimed he had found turned out to be a horse's tail. Cook and Conklin gave the camp another good story: Driving in on an old coyote trapper road to pick up a load of fossils, they encountered a couple of startled moonshiners. The 'shiners thought they were caught and jumped out of their car with rifles, but Cook just calmly drove around them.

By August 22, Gidley decided he had accomplished enough for the first season. The Smithsonian crew stored all its camp equipment in a warehouse located next to the Merit Store in Hagerman, an inexpensive alternative to shipping everything back the following summer. Gidley left on August 23 for Washington, D.C., where he planned to quickly clean and prepare the recovered fossils. But though he had sent five crates on the Oregon Short Line Railroad from Bliss on July 17, only four arrived at the museum on August 1. He was unaware of the lost box until his arrival at the Smithsonian in early September. On September 14, the museum shipping clerk sent a letter to the freight agent inquiring about the missing crate, but no reply came from Bliss. Angered by the railroad's disinterest, Assistant Secretary Wetmore also sent a letter to the freight agent in Bliss. Finally, almost a month after the shipping clerk's first letter, the railroad responded. The shipment was traced to Baltimore and delivered personally to Gidley on October 19, 1929.

Gidley's crew sent three tons of specimens to Washington that summer. Most were of a horse later named *Equus simplicidens* and included fossils of all ages and both sexes. Not only had the Smithsonian discovered the largest single sample of an extinct species of horse, it had also found the earliest known representative of the modern horse genus, *Equus*.

Maximum Yield Museums and universities from all corners of the country poured letters into the Smithsonian after the first season at Hagerman. Eager curators and paleontologists wanted details about the variety and number of fossils recovered, as well as future plans for the Horse Quarry. In response to a letter written by W. D. Matthew, chair of the Department of Paleontology at Berkeley, Wetmore outlined a second trip to Hagerman for early summer. He planned to send Gidley to the same Idaho sites opened the previous year. Wetmore wrote, "We expect to develop this site carefully so that the maximum yield of scientific material will be obtained ... and I believe that we shall have some material that we can let you have in exchange later."

In early May 1930, Gidley and his assistants traveled back to Hagerman to resume work at the quarry. Instead of the previous summer's devastating heat, the Smithsonian crew found themselves in the middle of a cold rainstorm. This year's camp included C. P. Singleton,

Samuel P. Wells, Elmer Cook, Frank Garnier, and J. Young Rogers. Singleton, making his second trip to the quarry, worked as chief field assistant. Wells, a graduate student from the University of California, received his first opportunity to work with the Smithsonian in Idaho. Cook returned, but his attendance was sporadic. Garnier came again as camp cook, but soon left as he had the year before. After a week's services, Gidley replaced him with Rogers.

The rain made the dirt roads slippery and hazardous, postponing the crew's trek to the high desert plateau near the fossil bone deposit the Smithsonian had worked in 1929. They spent five days indoors waiting for the weather to break. On May 9, sunshine offered a reprieve, and the men loaded their two-ton Ford truck with a week's rations, boxes, lumber, and thirty gallons of water. To reach camp, they had to cross the river on the main highway's bridge four miles south of Hagerman and then traverse twenty-five hilly miles over a rarely used dirt road. Part of this route followed the same path many pioneers took as they journeyed the historic Oregon Trail, and Gidley found three cast-iron hub-thimbles for the National Museum's collection during one of the biweekly trips to town for food, water, and materials.

With camp established, work began at the bone deposit situated at the southern edge of a short hill jutting out from the border of the plain. The party had to first remove overburden from the bone-bearing layers, often spending hours and even days shoveling the cross-bedded bands of coarse and fine sand to reach the fossil layer. As the crew uncovered bones, they brushed them clean, then saturated each with a thin solution of gum arabic. Gidley and his assistants further safeguarded the delicate bones by adhering burlap dipped in raw flour paste or thin plaster of paris. When dry, it formed a light, tough jacket similar to casts for broken human bones and necessary for packing and shipping to Washington, D.C. Cook ran out of plaster of paris once while casting fossils by himself. He built a fire to heat some gypsum and ground it up as a substitute. According to his son, Dick, the Smithsonian wrote and asked "what in the hell he cast those fossils in because they couldn't get it off."

Ending the second productive season at the Horse Quarry, Gidley was asked by a reporter if he had found human bones among the horses. His earlier discovery of a Pleistocene man at the Melbourne site in Florida had brewed a scientific storm. "If we had discovered any human bones," he replied, "we would have covered them up again quickly and hurried away in order to

As a student geologist, Neal Farmer used a Geiger counter like the one above to test a mastodon tooth he had found near Hagerman. It "pegged the meter," showing a maximum radioactivity reading. He later found that water-leached uranium had made every sample from the Horse Quarry "hot." Mining claims in the 1950s had sought fossils as a potential source of uranium to support Cold War security, what Farmer calls "fossils to fission." A government campaign even encouraged families to take Geiger counters along on picnics. Left: the Smithsonian's Norman H. Boss and colleague examine casted fossils at the Horse Quarry, 1931.

Inset: a geologist's rock hammer.

avoid any more trouble." Gidley never returned to Idaho. Illness kept him from leading a third Smithsonian dig at Hagerman, and he died in Washington, D.C., on September 26, 1931. His final journal article in 1930 for the National Museum about fossil excavation in Idaho not only conveyed an account of his work in Hagerman, but also revealed his passion for discovery: "To the fossil hunter such a deposit as the one here described is of much more than passing interest. First there is a satisfaction in working out a successful technique for collecting and preparing the bones for shipment to the laboratory; and there is the added keen pleasure of anticipation and expectation, as foot after foot and yard after yard of undisturbed ground is worked over, that the next bone to be discovered and developed will prove to be new to science or at least a better specimen than has before been found of an already known species."

Boise resident Richard P. Erwin shared Gidley's passion and had long believed scientists would someday discover Idaho as a field for investigation. He took a keen interest in the rock writings of Native Americans and considered all remnants of Idaho history important. Thinking the state museum should make efforts to acquire Hagerman Horse fossils, he asked the Idaho State Historical Society to seek a cooperative expedition with the Smithsonian in their upcoming 1931 season. When the board voted in favor of his idea, Erwin's wife wrote to Gidley inquiring if a joint effort would be agreeable. Gidley replied the decision was not his, but he could think of no reason why an agreement satisfactory to both parties could not be arranged. He believed the society would be better served by sending one representative rather than a group: "The natural result of two parties working the deposit at one time and dividing the material on the ground would be to separate permanently the more or less scattered bones of single specimens."

Gidley advised the Historical Society to contribute money to the expedition and send one man to receive instruction on proper methods of fossil bone collection. And he assured Mrs. Erwin the Boise Museum would obtain a liberal amount of fossil material for their contribution, as well as a better representation than the society could hope to get by undertaking the

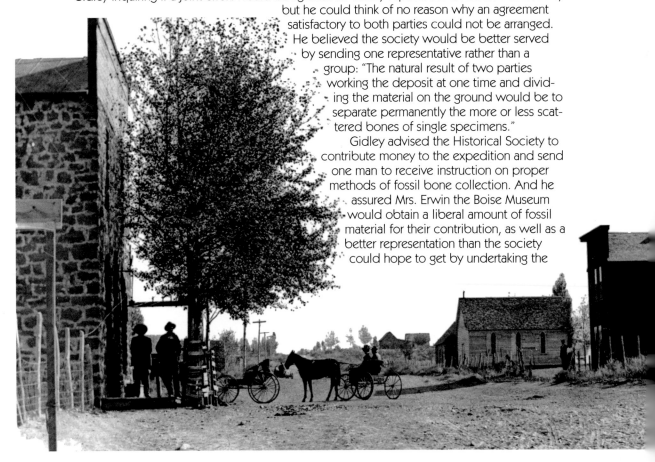

work independently. Mrs. Erwin shared Gidley's plan with the board members, and they approved it unanimously. The Historical Society quickly authorized a $200 contribution, hoping it would be enough to secure a good amount of fossil material for the state museum. On June 5, 1931, Assistant Secretary Wetmore officially welcomed their cooperation and accepted their donation.

By June 1, Smithsonian paleontologist Norman Boss had left Washington to begin the institution's third expedition. After arriving in Bliss on the 4th, he traveled by bus to Hagerman where he met crew members C. P. Singleton, Charles Bremmer, and C. W. Caldwell late in the evening. The group gathered equipment and supplies and left Hagerman on the 8th to establish camp near the Horse Quarry. Five days later, while Boss and his crew collected material left over from the previous year, the Historical Society hired Harold Tucker of the College of Idaho at Caldwell and sent him as their representative to the dig. In Tucker's first letter to the society, he wrote of three skulls and a jaw he helped uncover, as well as the harsh winds that blew all day. He was experiencing all facets of fossil collection: the removal of overburden, the search for the fossils, their retrieval from the ground, and their preparation for shipment. Also in the letter, Tucker requested gum arabic, ten gunnysacks, and fairly tough but not too heavy wrapping paper for casting and packing bones. He believed the items could be purchased in Boise and sent to the Smithsonian camp less expensively than they could be bought in Buhl or Twin Falls.

Hagerman street scenes, about 1909. Hagerman boomed long before the Smithsonian put it on the scientific map. Below: a high-wheeled International, the first car in Hagerman. Left: buggies parked at Billy Colthorp's saloon. Left above: Hagerman belt buckle.

The workforce stripped away enough overburden using a plow and a horse-drawn scraper (fresno) to reveal a bone-bearing layer approximately 500 square feet. With all the dirt removed, fossils emerged in abundance. By the end of July, the crew had recovered five complete horse skeletons, thirty-two skulls, forty-eight pairs of lower jaws, and numerous limb and foot bones in excellent condition representing both sexes and all stages of growth. They also found the fossil remains of birds, turtles, and fish, a season's work that filled thirty-seven boxes weighing 8,332 pounds.

On July 24, Tucker wrote to Boise informing the Historical Society of the current situation at the dig.

Boss wanted to break camp on August 3, so Tucker needed timber to build boxes for shipment and a truck to haul the fossils to Boise. He wrote of the Smithsonian's decision to give the society one-fifth of the material uncovered at the Horse Quarry, and he also reminded his employers of the work still ahead to prepare the fossils for display.

Before leaving Hagerman, the lean-faced, sun-darkened Boss sold all the Smithsonian's camp equipment. Nothing would be taken back to Washington or stored in Martin's Warehouse, a departure from years past. It seemed the Smithsonian had no further plans for the quarry, something Mrs. Erwin understood when she had asked to cooperate on the Smithsonian's "third and final trip."

While the Smithsonian excavated, the stock market crashed and the United States fell into economic depression. In 1932, when President Herbert Hoover could not spur the economy or lift the nation's spirits, the voters put their faith in Franklin D. Roosevelt. As a result of Roosevelt's New Deal legislation and the leadership of his secretary of the interior, Harold Ickes, the National Park Service became a more prominent federal agency. By the end of the 1930s, the number of areas governed by the Park Service more than doubled, permanent staff grew significantly, and the scope of its obligations greatly expanded. It assumed responsibility for preservation and jurisdiction over all memorials, military cemeteries, and battlefields. The guardians of Yosemite looked after the Statue of Liberty and Antietam as well with greater opportunities for historical interpretation. Park rangers could now do much more than merely guide visitors—they could reveal the essence of each site. The Park Service had entered a new era

when the Smithsonian sent Dr. C. Lewis Gazin, hired in 1932 as assistant curator of fossil mammals, on a final expedition to Hagerman.

On May 18, 1934, Gazin left Washington, D.C. by train and started the Smithsonian's fourth journey to the Snake River basin. Along the way, he stopped in Pittsburgh, Chicago, and Denver, touring the exhibit halls of local museums and visiting colleagues. George Sternburg and George Pearce met Gazin as he came off the train in Bliss on May 28. The three drove to Hagerman, bought groceries, and set up their camp near the same quarry worked by Gidley and Boss. Dick Cook remembers Gazin as "an old man with a white moustache, a white cap, white shirt, white pants, everything was white." In spite of the dig's demands, the scientist took time to set the small boy on his knee, tell him stories, and give him gum.

Hagerman's Masonic Hall now resides where Colthorp's saloon once held sway. Left: Hagerman stores its history on Main Street in the valley's Historical Society Museum.

Gazin found the quarry in extremely poor condition, mostly owing to wind-blown sand and the cave-in of the forty-five-feet-high back wall worked three years previously by Boss. The men would have to remove a substantial amount of overburden to reach the bone-bearing layer. Gazin hired Harry Hall, a local prospector and experienced miner, to blast out a large section of the back wall, and Richard Clifford used his workhorse-drawn fresno to remove debris from the quarry. In that debris lay the mighty mastodon's skull and jaws. While

Hall and Clifford took out tons of dirt, Gazin, Pearce, and Elmer Cook prospected other sites near the camp. The group recovered various horse fossils, the skull of an extinct species of antelope, the skulls and lower jaws of large beaver, and the bones of a pumalike cat.

On July 1, more than

Hagerman liquor traffic. Fossil hunter Elmer Cook and friends stage a mock hold-up at Colthorp's saloon. Right: Billy Colthorp's modern counterpart, Wilson's Club in downtown Hagerman.

thirty days after Hall and Clifford began clearing the Horse Quarry with picks, shovels, and scrapers, it was ready for excavation with whiskbrooms and awls. Gazin described the quarry in detail: "The exposed surface of the fossil bed was in plan the shape of a crescent about 55 feet between tips and about 18 feet from front to back across the widest portion. The back wall rose from both ends of the cut to a point somewhat over 50 feet higher than the middle of the bone layer. The dump in front of the quarry extended some 50 or 60 feet out from the edge of the bone layer and represented the accumulated debris of three seasons of quarrying in addition to the material moved during the present season." Because of the high concentration of bones, large blocks of earth had to be taken up and carefully bound in burlap and plaster of paris. Though Gazin's party unearthed the remains of many different animals, the bulk of the fossils collected belonged to the extinct horse, *Equus simplicidens*.

Prospecting the bluffs south of the quarry along the west side of the Snake River, the crew found other animal bones in the well-exposed formation. Within its sandy slopes they encountered the widest variety of fossil remains found during the expedition, among them a shrew, a small dog about the size of a coyote, a saber-tooth cat, a large otter, beaver, muskrats, ground squirrels, rabbits, ground sloths, mastodons, and two species of camel. In addition to the mammals, they found an assortment of birds, turtles, snakes, frogs, and fish. Gazin specifically mentioned the skeletal remains of three peccaries uncovered by Pearce: "an adult and two young huddled together almost as in life" that looked complete.

By August 5, Gazin and his group began making crates to ship all the fossils they had collected. They built thirty-six boxes from 820 feet of lumber, and used over 1,200 pounds

of plaster of paris in order to ready the 15,000 pounds of fossils for the train ride to Washington, D.C. By the 16th the bones were sent, and Gazin traveled to other locations prospecting for more material. After searching near the Bruneau River, Grand View, and Stinker Creek, he decided to end the season.

Between 1934 and 1938, Gazin published articles on fossil shrews, mustelids, sloths, hares, and horses from the early Pliocene collected in Idaho. His efforts, combined with the work of Gidley and Boss, seemed to cover all points of interest in the area. Since the Smithsonian had more than enough fossils to exchange with interested museums across the country, it appeared further explorations and writings concerning the deposits at Hagerman could only be an act of repetition.

Systematically Looted

More than twenty years after the final Smithsonian excavation in 1934, the steep bluffs opposite Hagerman once again crawled with scientists. This time attention centered not on the larger specimens but on the critically important small Pliocene fauna like snails and rodents. Claude Hibbard and Dwight Taylor spent several seasons exploring the Hagerman Fossil Beds during the late 1950s and 1960s and collaborated on a series of journal articles. Hibbard, working for the University of Michigan, wrote on insectivores, rabbits, and rodents from the Pliocene found in Idaho. Aldrich Bowler, who brought his young son Peter out to work on the excavations, described the paleontologist as "tall and dark, a very striking man." Dick Cook recalled Hibbard's aversion to buzzards: "The worst thing he ever studied. They would puke and stink—he said it was his worst assignment." Taylor, working for the U.S. Geological Survey, wrote extensively on snails. Hibbard's and Taylor's cooperative articles provided a detailed study of Pliocene and Pleistocene faunas in the western United States. They aimed to advance the knowledge of the geologic range and stratigraphic value of many fossils and to create a more solid foundation for environmental interpretation of fossil deposits. Their work helped establish Hagerman not only as a source for horse fossils, but also as a world standard in Pliocene fauna.

James Reid Macdonald had long carried an ambition to reopen the Smithsonian Horse Quarry and collect a representation for the Natural History Museum of Los Angeles County. The opportunity eluded him until after his museum's work in the Anza-Borrego Desert, when a Hagerman collection became a "must" for comparison with the fossils excavated there. On June 1, 1966, Macdonald and Floyd Humeston left California and traveled to Idaho. They organized camp near the edge of the Snake River across from the striking falls of Thousand Springs. Unlike the Smithsonian excavators, Macdonald had a bulldozer to remove overburden and level the quarry face. After a day with the bulldozer, Macdonald, helped by University of Michigan students under the direction of Hibbard, spent a week shoveling the coarse-grained sand and clay. The group uncovered an average of a skull a day, with the other skeletal remains jumbled together in the ancient sand bar. Students found fossils in solid concretions and in soft sand, but all specimens had to be carefully handled and untangled in proper sequence to preserve as much of the bone as possible. By the end of June their finds included twenty-five horse skulls, a colt skeleton, and a huge pile of miscellaneous bones representing a great many animals from the fauna, certainly more than enough to compare with the Anza-Borrego material.

John H. White, curator of vertebrate paleontology at the Idaho Natural History Museum, decided to conduct excavations at Hagerman the following year. With the help of Dave Fortsch, White began work in early June 1967. Like the Gidley party of 1931, they had to postpone the removal of overburden due to poor weather conditions. It rained for about a week before efforts could begin in both the quarry opened by the Los Angeles County Museum and a new area west of the site. White uncovered about a dozen skulls and numerous other bones during the nineteen-day excavation, a fair amount for the Pocatello museum.

Rediscovery of the Hagerman sites spiked the controversy anew over disbursement of Idaho's fossils. Like Althea Fouch in 1935, columnist Jim MacLean decried the absence of any laws preventing shipment of fossils to out-of-state museums. Writing in 1954, he called the Smithsonian expeditions "raids" and claimed Idaho had been "systematically looted for 30 years of tons of priceless fossils showcased in museums across the United States." Lack of money compounded the lack of laws. Mrs. Vietta Anderson of Burley offered the Idaho Historical Society full rights to the complete skeleton of a sixteen-feet-tall mastodon discovered on her farm. When Idaho could not raise the $1,500 to excavate, ship, and set up the fossil, Utah got it.

A 1914 team of excavators uses a tripod to lift fossils. Bones in protective plaster casts could weigh hundreds of pounds and required creative transportation. Left: horsepower hauls a fossil-heavy sled at the Horse Quarry, 1929. Left above: the Smithsonian's centennial stamp.

In 1968, a year after his excavation, White proposed a state park at Hagerman. "I'm no promoter," he said, "but I think this is a jewel. We've got something here Disneyland would love to have." But private agricultural and irrigation development kept pace with efforts to preserve the area. In 1974, the National Park Service completed a report requested by Idaho's congressional delegation. By then a massive irrigation pipe sys-

tem lay almost through the middle of the fossil beds. The Park Service proposed three options—a state park, a state park and federal cooperative zone, or a national monument—

Irrigation seepage sprouts greenery on bluffs that Smithsonian expeditions saw covered with sagebrush. Right: a student paleontologist sifts Hagerman hills for fossilized tortoise fragments.

and the debate sharpened. Two years later, Sen. James McClure chaired a hearing at Hagerman over legislation he had introduced with Sen. Frank Church to create a national monument there. Farmers claimed the site "nobody seems to want" certainly did not warrant sacrificing "development of thousands of acres of valuable farmland." Harry LeMoyne, president of Yahoo Mutual and Tuana Mutual irrigation companies, thought "equipping a national monument with a tourist facility would cost millions of dollars but a few dollars would suffice for scientific preservation." *The Idaho Statesman* editorial on December 22, 1976, defended the proposal, saying it was not necessary to sacrifice a "historical treasure" when the land for the monument was a modest 5,500 acres compared to "hundreds of thousands of acres of potential farmland in southern Idaho suitable for development over the years." As for cost, the editorial felt national rather than state management could better provide funding for this significant and invaluable resource.

Finally in 1988, nearly sixty years after the first Smithsonian excavation, Congress established the bluffs along the Snake River as the Hagerman Fossil Beds National Monument. Because of the area's unique variety, quantity, and quality of fossils, the government set aside 4,281 acres "to preserve for the benefit and enjoyment of present and future generations the outstanding paleontological sites known as the Hagerman Valley fossil sites, to provide a center for continuing paleontological research, and to provide for the display and interpretation of the scientific specimens uncovered at such sites." But according to Aldrich Bowler, "They had a bad map, so they set up a preserve that preserved the pipe." The original lines had to be redrawn since they followed the pipeline right through the bone quarry. Decades of irrigation on surrounding farmland had seeped down and eaten at the bluffs. "It takes a long time," said Bowler in 1996, "but water will go all the way through it." More than a hundred years after Yellowstone, preservation still battled use.

Pragmatic Alliances

Conservation gave a young nation historical significance. It drove the creation of national parks to satisfy American longing for heritage. Historian Alfred Runte wrote in 1976, "When national parks were first established, protection of the 'environment' as now defined was the least of preservationists' aims. Rather America's incentive for the national park idea lay in the persistence of a painfully felt desire for time-honored traditions in the United States. For decades the nation had suffered the embarrassment of a dearth of recognized cultural achievements."

Americans adopted the West's wilderness as a surrogate for cultural achievement. Ageless wonderlands became the observable symbol of permanence and stability for the new nation, and science likewise lent itself to America's developing national pride. President Thomas Jefferson, angered by French claims that the animals of the New World were feeble and small, sent the skeleton of an enormous moose to France to demonstrate the magnitude and strength of wild American beasts. Natural science and natural history fed the fledgling national ego.

Hagerman's fossil quarries, significant for their diverse and abundant record of the late Pliocene, reflect the conservationist mood that swept America in the late nineteenth and

twentieth centuries. That strong sentiment led to the creation of forty-eight national parks and numerous monuments, preserves, lakeshores, rivers, seashores, historic sites, memorials, military battlefield parks, historical parks, recreation areas, and parkways. The goal, according to public-land theorist Joseph Sax, was "to preserve the spectacular sites for the average citizen by holding them as public places to be enjoyed by all." But preservation has also made

Sandy river slopes hide the Horse Quarry where preservation and use play out a centuries-old story. Above: the seal set into the floor of the Smithsonian Castle.

what Runte called a "pragmatic alliance" with use. At Hagerman, paleontological discovery evolved into a knowledge of past environments that gives insight into present environmental problems. The management of natural resources there creates cultural assets. The story of the Smithsonian Horse Quarry excavations does more than illustrate scientific trends or explain procedures for fossil preservation. It unearths a lost world that helped create a new one.

◆

Todd Shallat, Ph.D.
History, Boise State University
James Frost, Ph D.
Photographer, Black Canyon Communications

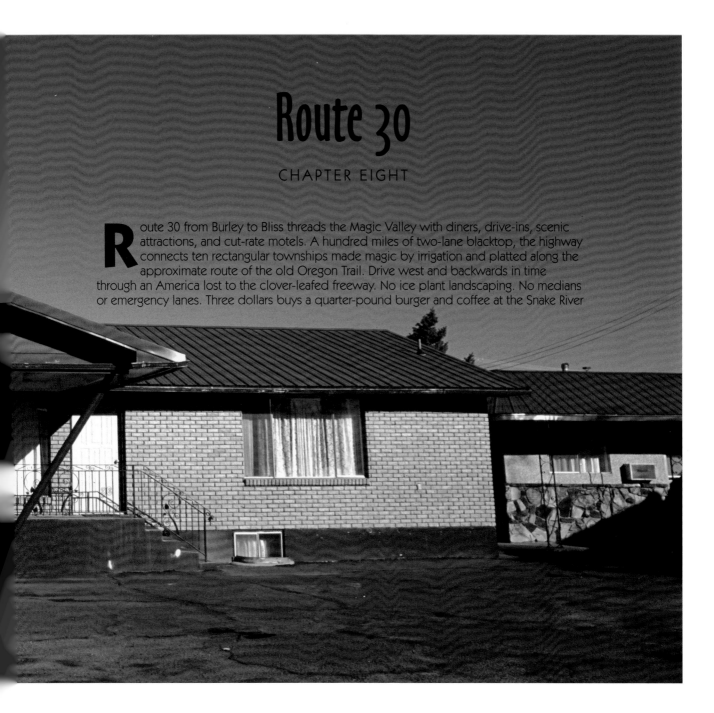

Route 30

CHAPTER EIGHT

Route 30 from Burley to Bliss threads the Magic Valley with diners, drive-ins, scenic attractions, and cut-rate motels. A hundred miles of two-lane blacktop, the highway connects ten rectangular townships made magic by irrigation and platted along the approximate route of the old Oregon Trail. Drive west and backwards in time through an America lost to the clover-leafed freeway. No ice plant landscaping. No medians or emergency lanes. Three dollars buys a quarter-pound burger and coffee at the Snake River

Lounge in Burley. Crinkle fries round out a foot-long hotdog at Crowley's in Twin Falls. Fill up the Ford in Filer. Turn north at the Black Bear Bar and dip through the Hagerman Valley where Bonneville boulders, farmers maintain, are petrified watermelons, where poplars planted as windbreaks run straight as meridian lines.

Paved from 1927 to 1935, the highway recalls a nation's infatuation with cars and car culture in an era when touring by motor coach became a leisurely alternative to coast-to-coast travel by rail. The railroad sacrificed scenery to velocity. Trains were "uncomfortable necessities which must be employed upon occasion because we live in an unimaginably commercial world," said Robert Sloss, a motor tourist. For author Theodore Dreiser, writing in 1916, the railroads had become "huge, clumsy affairs little suited to the temperamental needs and moods of the average human being." But motoring, being slower and more independent, reduced the

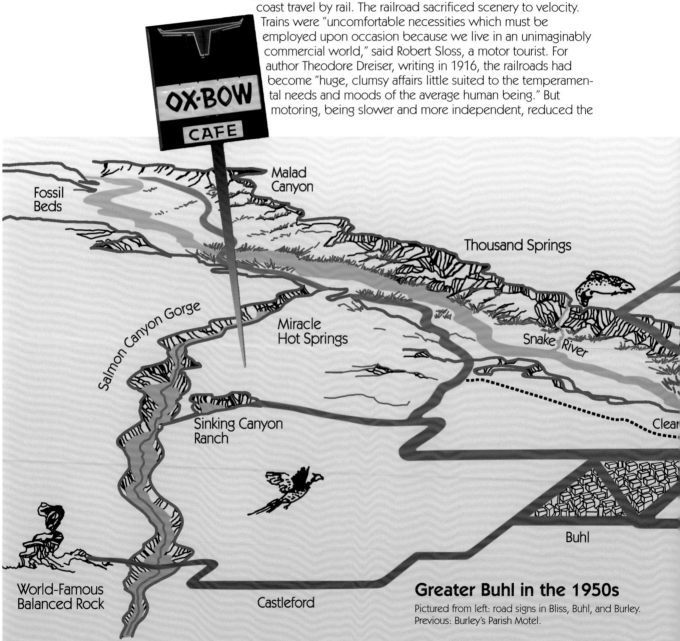

Greater Buhl in the 1950s
Pictured from left: road signs in Bliss, Buhl, and Burley.
Previous: Burley's Parish Motel.

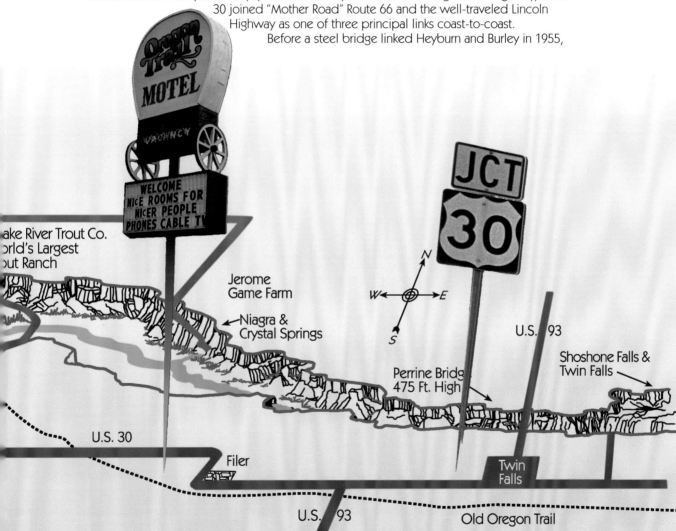

wonder of transcontinental travel to a human scale. "We are seeing the country for the first time," wrote Emily Post.

Already in 1914 a bus line out of Shoshone reached Twin Falls on an oiled highway. After Congress passed the 1921 Federal Highway Act creating the interstate system, tourists crossed west from Carey, Shoshone, Gooding, and Bliss on snowy U.S. 20 via Yellowstone National Park. To the south was the Lincoln Highway from New Jersey to San Francisco, an ocean-to-ocean connection that bypassed the Pacific Northwest. Idaho and Oregon demanded a northern all-weather interstate. Winter, the states protested, closed the switch-back Yellowstone passes, and the park charged an admittance fee of $7.50 per car. The compromise hammered out by the U.S. Bureau of Roads was a spur off the Lincoln Highway called U.S. 30 North, now simply U.S. 30. Locally known as the Oregon Trail Highway, Route 30 joined "Mother Road" Route 66 and the well-traveled Lincoln Highway as one of three principal links coast-to-coast.

Before a steel bridge linked Heyburn and Burley in 1955,

motorists from the east entered the Magic Valley on a vibrating timber truss. Burley—a farm town named for its rail agent and chartered in 1906—had been the empty intersection of the

Oregon Short Line and the gold road to California before the U.S. Reclamation Service built Minidoka Dam. A processing and shipping center for sugar beets and potatoes, the Burley area in 1942 lured thousands of Mexican *braceros*, Japanese American field workers from Camp Minidoka, and even German prisoners of war. In 1947, however, city fathers warned that the future would be stunted if Congress failed to green Cassia County with water stored by the dam. "What is needed is 50,000 more votes to make the folks back in Washington bring pressure on the reclamation service," protested a

city official. "We need more land under water," he said, "to produce the food the nation needs." Still, the town with its motels and neon Main Street buzzed with automobiles. The 1950 census showed that 5,924 Burley residents owned 5,200 motor vehicles, nearly twice the national average. Traffic fatalities kept pace. Statewide numbers showed an astounding death-per-mileage rate of seven fatal collisions per one hundred-million-highway miles.

Rail crossings and hairpin turns made Route 30 especially deadly in the postwar forties. Glenn Buckendorf, a high school senior in 1947, remembers a hazard called Deadman's Corner between Filer and Buhl. "That was before the corners were banked or contoured," says

Hagerman poplars planted as windbreaks characterize the so-called "Mormon landscape" of island townships in checkerboard fields. Right: coffee, 2 bits in Bliss. Left: teardrop streamlining of the 1950 Ford featured "fingertip steering" and "magic-action brakes."

Buckendorf. "People were always trying to pass a tractor or hay truck. Where the highway turned, some [people] kept going straight."

Buckendorf, whose father opened Buckendorf's Tire Service off the highway in Buhl, recalls seeing Gene Autry and *Gone With the Wind* for a nickel in the 1927 Ramona Theater—now a restaurant and the last remaining Moorish-style movie house in the state. In 1942, wartime gas and tire rationing kept teenagers off the highway. After 1945, however, "farm kids had plenty of cars." One of the first drive-in type restaurants was a hamburger place called Papenfuss, a high school hangout. Buckendorf also recalls drive-in movies on Moon Glow Road.

Buhl, the hometown of trout farming, thrived in the postwar era. So did county seat Twin Falls. Although a Hooverville called Shanty Town and the local custom of rolling junk cars off steep cliffs had long since tarnished the magic landscape, World War II and the construction of Camp Minidoka flooded the city with jobs. With a population of 17,000 in 1947, Twin boasted $190 million in agricultural exports. Wool, dairy, wheat, barley, fruit, potatoes, seed beans, and abundant fishing and boating made the farm hub "Idaho's bright spot for vacations or vocations," according to a booster's brochure. Car dealers milked the boom from glassy auto showrooms. Herriott's Auto Sales on Second

Twin Falls in 1956 boasted fifty warehouses, forty manufacturing establishments, twenty-four churches, ten parks, nine schools, and three museums. Left: Price Hardware on Main Avenue West. Below: a Moderne service station later housed a tire outlet.

Avenue had more than 200 feet of plate glass windows and a car freight elevator to a second floor repair shop. Gooding Motors sold Chevrolets from a Main Street palace with curbside gas pumps.

Clean lines suggested clean service in the angular aerodynamics of a Twin Falls motel and a Heyburn gas station's abandoned carport. Right: Smith's Dairy, Buhl, established in 1944, renovated in 1969.

Route 30 along Fourth Avenue sprouted boxlike, deck-roofed, Moderne-style diners and canopied service stations. In 1957, less than a year after President Dwight Eisenhower signed a $27 billion nationwide master plan for uniform superhighways, Twin Falls was congested enough to couple Route 30 southbound via Second Avenue and northbound via Main.

Federal aid for Idaho highways quadrupled to $20 million annually during the 1950s. The 1956 Interstate Highway Act, among the most ambitious public works ever attempted, committed the government to pay ninety percent of 41,000 miles of toll-free roads. Engineers imagined "magic motorways" with free-flowing traffic diverted around or away from gas-pump towns. Freeways, proponents believed, would boost the efficiency of the American economy and arrest urban decay. But technology's progress has never been seamless in Idaho's fractured valley. Broken like the fossil record and progressing in fits and jumps, the interstate system turned the Malta–to–Burley–to–Bliss leg of old Route 30 into a "local service" highway under the care of the state. Work on Interstate 80 (now called I-84) stalled between Glenns Ferry and Hammet. Not until the 1970s could the freeway driver race past the Magic Valley. Not until 1981, when Caldwell retired its last interstate stoplight, could a driver span the desert without breaking for Idaho towns.

"Thanks to the interstate highway system," said journalist Charles Kuralt, "it is now possible to travel across the country from coast to coast without see- ing any- thing. From the

interstate America is all steel guardrails and plastic signs, and every place

Bob's Museum, Bliss. The rock and gift shop is a creative merchandising effort free of corporate influence. No video taping or electronic scanners here. Shoppers browse uninterrupted, trusted to pay even when Bob is out. Left: last bar for one mile, west of Buhl. Below: fossil-fuel dinosaur, Bliss.

looks and feels and sounds and smells like every other place."

But not like old Route 30. Still a remnant of a roadside culture lost elsewhere to standardization, the small-town highway reveals secrets of the Magic Valley that freeway travelers will never know.

◆

Todd Shallat, Ph.D.
History, Boise State University

Making Magic

CHAPTER NINE

Down the Boise, the Big Lost, the Blackfoot,
The Raft, the Rock, the Burnt, the Dry, the Silver, the Selway, the Salmon;
Down Henrys Fork and Jackson Hole;
Down rivulets that seep and vanish, inching through porous strata;
Down the Idaho face of the Rockies, surging with Yellowstone's snowmelt;
Carrying half the Columbia and twice the volume of the Colorado;
Curving 1,078 miles through a basin larger than Utah;
Lighting subdivisions from Seattle to San Diego;

Irrigating four million acres;

Leading the nation (perhaps even the world) in per capita

water consumption ... the Snake in a blistering August is a torrent severed in half. At Milner Dam above Twin Falls a child can hop the streambed. In drought, the only water that escapes irrigation is the seepage through cracks in the dam.

Granite torn from the cliffs bakes in the Milner streambed. Worldviews collide. "It makes me feel good," says a man who can channel the equivalent flow of 1,900 residential fire hydrants (3,800 cubic feet per second) into Milner's South Side Canal. Born in Wendell and raised in Jerome, Vince Alberdi manages the most concrete result of a 1903 handshake that joined banker Stanley Milner and farmer Ira Perrine in the legendary corporation that built the low rubble dam. Today the Milner-Perrine Twin Falls Canal Company back-floods the Snake about thirty-four miles from Murtaugh to the outskirts of Burley. Through 1,000 miles of coulees, ditches, and drains, the lifeblood of agribusiness pitchforks south and west into 204,000 acres of cropland. About 3,000 headgates serve 4,000 shareholders. In six months at full capacity the system can deliver more than one million acre-feet. That's 325 billion gallons—enough water to flood Manhattan to the base of Miss Liberty's torch.

Harvesting onions near Twin Falls, about 1945. Previous: Clayton Fetzer, foreground, and Dan Paslay move water lines on their 62-acre alfalfa field near Paul in Minidoka County.

"We've been able to capture the river," Alberdi believes. "We not only provide the livelihood for several thousand people, but we provide the much needed food for our population as well." Benefits include the state's leading barley harvest plus wheat, corn, oats, sugar beets, dry beans, peas, sweet cherries, apricots, and alfalfa. To the north a sibling canal feeds 170,000 acres of mostly volcanic soils famous for Russet potatoes. Annually, 197,000 cows from 403 area dairies produce 4.2 billion gallons of milk.

Not bad for a leaky dam.

Sherl L. Chapman of the Idaho Water Users Association credits the system that Milner inspired with a farming bonanza worth $5.3 billion a year. "The development of Idaho's irrigation capacity is the single most significant activity in the history of our state," says Chapman, a farm lobbyist and good at his job. Rivals would surely agree that sweet deals for irrigators have been politically significant, even dominant. Chapman admits to tradeoffs: Milner Dam choked Shoshone Falls but opened 260,000 acres—a worthy sacrifice considering the "true miracle" of ditch irrigation, and doubly miraculous because "the vast majority of the system's been put in place in what is really a relatively short period of time compared to historical standards." In seventy-three years, 1902 to 1975, the nation's tenth-longest river lured twenty-five main-stem dams and fifty, maybe sixty, upland water projects. Too short a time, say critics. Too short for engineers to foresee the workings of a natural law immutably basic to river construction: the revenge of technological systems through the law of unintended effects.

The revenge of the system continued in dank lagoons that trapped and settled agricultural runoff like a staircase of septic tanks. By

1976, when the collapse of Teton Dam ended the era of big reclamation, fully half of the thundering Snake (508 miles) had been flattened in storage lakes. In time that flatwater stewed with chemical toxins. Ditch water added topsoil. Nitrates fed algae blooms. Dams, ecologists said, devastated the Snake in ways too profound to calculate trade-offs. Dams killed the rapids and rills that cooled and cleansed the river. Dams quelled seasonal flooding, crashing the energy loop that replenished river plankton. Dams flooded out minks and marmots. Dams disoriented the migrating salmon, and dams muddied the sandy places that trout used for spawning grounds.

It's a mighty hard road that
  my poor hands have hoed.
My poor feet have traveled
  the hot dusty road.
On the edge of the city you
  see me and then,
I come with the dust and I go
  with the wind.
                    -Woody Guthrie,
                        about 1932

Seasonal workers near I-84. Above: cast-iron harvester seat, Jerome.

Most tragic of all, said ecologists in the 1980s, were the ninety-four effluent miles from Milner to King Hill. Here in the canyon heart of the Magic Valley, the Snake still harbored the continent's largest freshwater fish, the white

Perrine Bridge, 1927. The cantilever truss spanned the Snake with 98,750 steel parts weighing 2,900 tons. Left: Peter Kimberly (sitting) and Frank Buhl (standing right) at Rock Creek siphon, 1905.

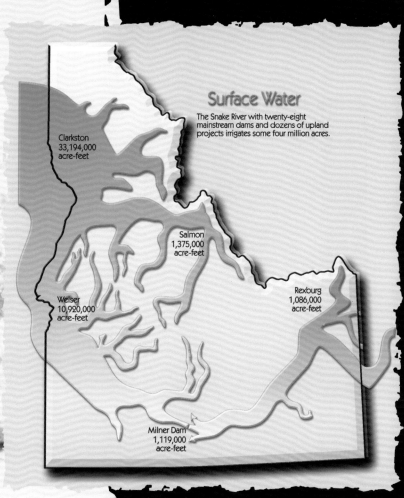

Surface Water

The Snake River with twenty-eight mainstream dams and dozens of upland projects irrigates some four million acres.

Clarkston
33,194,000
acre-feet

Salmon
1,375,000
acre-feet

Rexburg
1,086,000
acre-feet

Weiser
10,920,000
acre-feet

Milner Dam
1,119,000
acre-feet

An Engineer's Creation

Summer flows at Milner Dam plummeted from 2,000 cubic feet per second in 1911 to near zero in the 1920s. Severed by dams, drained for irrigation, replenished by tributaries and literally thousands of springs, the Snake, writes conservationist Tim Palmer, "may be our foremost example of a river that is repeatedly killed off but repeatedly returns to life."

sturgeon—some older than Idaho statehood and longer than a fisherman's skiff. Here the hackberry thickets clattered with thousands of songbirds. Mallards nested the tules. Blue-gray

herons, hooked-necked and dangle-footed, cruised the backwater low as if skimming under radar. And here, according to a 1988 report from the Idaho Department of Health and Welfare, the Snake was an open sewer. Outboards fouled in floating mats of rope-like filament algae. Toxins layered the streambed—enough herbicide, pesticide, ammonia, mercury, copper, and organic matter to contaminate the Snake River aquifer and threaten drinking supplies. In 1998 the Nature Conservancy called the

Milner–to–King Hill reach "the most polluted and degraded in Idaho." State officials conceded that "a water-quality-limited segment" had suffered "aquatic ecosystem degradation." Greens found stronger words: "Blow the dams. Let the river run and re-learn how to live like a river instead of like a barren canal for barges and a source of cheap electricity," raged an editorial in the *Idaho Mountain Express,* as if the Snake were Love Canal.

"We set out to tame the rivers," wrote Marc Reisner in *Cadillac Desert.* "We set out to make the future of the American West secure; what we really did was make ourselves rich and our descendants insecure."

Parched riverbed below Milner Dam. Above: bridge worker dangles from the canyon rim some 550 feet above the Snake near Twin Falls, about 1927.

Nowhere is that future harder to read than on the torrent of great expectations the trappers called "savage" and "mad." Shrouded in myth and romance, the Snake begs simplification. Farmers marvel at concrete wonders that cultivated a wasteland. Greens see paradise lost. Either way, the discourse

is narrowly framed on the impact of infrastructure, as if technology drove history, as if construction overrode human judgment or brought life to a lifeless place. A beast, a benefactor,

A crop duster sprays for aphids, raising concern over the health-risks of potato crop pesticides. Right: valley-grown alfalfa fuels a statewide dairy industry with some 15,000 workers and annual revenues approaching $800 million.

the rubble colossus of the Magic Valley poses difficult questions about the worth of the predammed desert in Idaho's primordial state. From where in Idaho's past do we measure technology's progress? Progress from where to what?

Below Milner's spillway any measure of technology's progress must contend with movement and flux. Authors in these pages have probed secrets of a mobile landscape. Flattened by lava and blasted into angular chasms by Lake Bonneville's swirling deluge, the magical valley poses a challenge to Darwinian notions of linear progress with its deep and remarkable records of cataclysmic change. Because the region also holds some of the continent's oldest-known records of Stone Age civilization, the valley tells hopeful stories: a history of coping and adaptation through ice and drought and global warming, a 13,000-year epic of the human encounter with catastrophic events. Idaho in that time has thawed into arid grasslands. Horses have returned. Storms have tossed boulders larger than bison. Cliffs have broken off in an instant. Since the evidence of the human response mostly predates the written record, history, like the story of *Equus*, suggests a number of possible patterns too fleeting and incomplete for

science to carefully draw. "The ecosystem," said ecologist Frank Egler, a critic of Darwinian sequence, "is not more complex than we think; it is more complex than we can think." Likewise the patterns of human progress are harder to know than we think—than we can think—on the lava steppe of the Snake.

About the most the historian can hope to know about the Magic Valley's pattern of progress is how people from different places perceived their migrating world. How it was, for example, that the geologist King stumbled upon the sublime at the brink of a lava canyon. How it was that an Oregon-bound Missouri farm boy imagined the Devil's Backbone. How boosters discovered Richfield, Goshen, Bliss, Paradise Valley, and Eden. How publicists for the Union Pacific framed industrial farming. How Basques found a shepherd's kingdom. How Latter-day Saints from Utah found in Cassia County a New World province of Zion.

Families line up for big smokeys and super spuds in Rupert's town square on Independence Day.

Nature is perception. Nature in the magical valley is also a story passionately told about engineering sensations—about the steel and concrete that ravaged or rescued the primordial Canaan of wondrous terrain. Said a contributor to *Atlantic Monthly* in the year the first wagons of saints unloaded in Cassia County: "We have grown accustomed to finding whatever we please in the landscape, and read in it what we have in our own hearts."

◆

iG "SMOKEY" - A BARBEQUE GLAZED SAUSAGE

Secrets of the Magic Valley

Sources/Credits

Chapter 1: Magic Mirror

Bowler, Peter A., "The Middle Snake River: Ecological Risk Assessment and Strategies for Recovery," Presented at the U.S. Environmental Protection Agency's Fourth National Conference on Water Quality Criteria and Standards for the 21st Century, September 1994; **Farmer**, Neal, Interview by K. Baxter, 15 September 2000 ["To leak or not to leak," "the landslide capital of Idaho," "mix in water"]; **Fiege**, Mark, *Irrigated Eden: The Making of an Agricultural Landscape in the American West* (Seattle: University of Washington Press, 1999) ["problematic relationship" p. 10, "not just a place" p. 102, "half a million horses" p. 179, "activities are not always opposed to nature" p. 208]; **Fisher**, Vardis, *Idaho: A Guide in Word and Picture* (New York: Oxford University Press, 1950) ["topographically strange" p. 41, "so appalling" p. 208];**"The Thousand Springs and Other Things,"** Hagerman, vertical files, Idaho State Historical Library and Archives ["man the magician" p. 5]; **Lane**, Belden, *Landscapes of the Sacred* (New York: Paulist Press, 1943) [Wallace Stegner "geography of hope" p. ix]; **Link**, Paul, "Geology of Hagerman Fossil Beds National Monument and Vicinity," Idaho State University (1999); **MacLean**, Norman, *A River Runs Through It* (Chicago: University of Chicago Press, 1976); **Penson**, Betty, "Are Thousand Springs Going Down the Drain?" *The Idaho Statesman* 23 August 1970, p. 4-B [Keith Higginson "no one owns water," Norman Standal "increased Horsetail Falls" and "clear as a swimming pool," Bruce Bowler "scar the landscape" and "not a thousand," Aldrich Bowler "very secretive," Glenn J. Hall "The plant does not consume"]; **Rhodenbaugh**, Harold, *The Idaho Statesman*, 20 January 1929 ["Nature is dramatic"]; **Ryan**, Don, "New cash crop has big teeth," *The Idaho Statesman*, 2001; **Shallat**, Todd, ed., *Snake: The Plain and Its People* (Boise, Idaho: Boise State University, 1994); **Turner**, Frederick Jackson, "The Significance of the Frontier in American History," *Proceedings of the State Historical Society of Wisconsin*, July 12, 1893 ["that dominant individualism" p. 225]; **Woods**, Spencer, "Hydrology of the Hagerman Area: Thousand Springs and Water Development on the Snake River," Boise State University (1998); **Woodward**, Tim, "Tropical fish in Idaho," *The Idaho Statesman*, 9 April 2001, Main, p. 1, 9; **Worster**, Donald, *Under Western Skies* (New York: Oxford University Press, 1992) ["modern agribusiness" p. 29, "lives or dies" p. 30].

Chapter 2: *Equus* Evolves

Behrensmeyer, A. K., "Taphonomic and Ecological Information from Bone Weathering," *Paleobiology* 4 (1978): 150-162; **Erz**, W., "Tooth Eruption and Replacement in Burchell's Zebra, *Equus burchelli* Gray 1825," *Arnoldia* 1, no. 22 (1964): 1-8; **Gazin**, C. L., "A Study of the Fossil Horse Remains from the Upper Pliocene of Idaho," *Proceedings United States National Museum* 83 (1985): 281-320; **Hermanson**, J. W. and B. J. MacFadden, "Evolutionary and Functional Morphology of the Shoulder Region and Stay-Apparatus In Fossil and Extant Horses (*Equidae*)," *Journal of Vertebrate Paleontology* 12, no. 3 (1992): 377-386; **Jeffery**, Dale, *Horse Dentistry: The Theory and Practice of Equine Dental Maintenance* (Norfolk, Nebraska: Norfolk Printing Co., 1996); **Klingel**, H. and U. Klingel, "Tooth Development and Age Determination in the Plains Zebra (*Equus quagga boehmi* Matschie)," *Der Zoologische Garten* 33, no. 1-3 (1966): 34-54; **Lindsay**, E. H., N. D. Opdyke, and N. M. Johnson, "Pliocene Dispersal of the Horse *Equus* and Late Cenozoic Mammalian Dispersal Events," *Nature* 287 (1980): 135-138; **Lindsay**, E. H., N. D. Opdyke, and N. M. Johnson, "Blancan-Hemphillian Land Mammal Ages and Late Cenozoic Mammal Dispersal Events," *Annual Reviews of Earth and Planetary Science* 12 (1984): 445-488; **MacFadden**, B. J., *Fossil Horses: Systematics, Paleobiology and Evolution of the Family* Equidae (New York: Cambridge University Press, 1992); **Myers**, V. S. and J. K. Burt, "The Radiographic Location of Epiphyseal Lines in Equine Limbs," *Proceedings of the 12th Annual Convention of the American Association of Equine Practitioners* (1966): 21-39; **Scott**, W. B., *The Theory of Evolution* (New York: MacMillan, 1917) ["everything has been sacrificed" p. 46]; **Smith**, G. R. and W. P. Patterson, "Milo-Pliocene Seasonality On The Snake River Plain: Comparison of Faunal and Oxygen Isotopic Evidence," *Palaeogeography, Palaeoclimatology, Palaeoecology* 107 (1994): 291-302; **Smuts**, G. L. "Population Characteristics of Burchell's Zebra (*Equus burchelli antiquorum* H. Smith 1841) in the Kruger National Park," *South African Journal of Wildlife Research* 6 (1976): 99-112; **Spinage**, C. A. "Age Estimation of Zebra," *East African Wildlife Journal* 10 (1972): 273-277.

Chapter 3: Arrows and Atlatls

Ames, Kenneth M., *Idaho Archaeologist* 4(1-2): 1-10; **Butler**, B. Robert, *Handbook of North American Indians Volume II*, W. L. Azevedo, ed. (Washington, D.C.: Smithsonian Institution, 1986); **Butler**, B. Robert and Kelly Murphey, "Kanaka Rapids Hydroelectric Project, Phase II Cultural Resource," *B. R. Butler Associates Report*, Pocatello, Idaho (1968): 82-83; **Crabtree**, Don E., "Archaeological Evidence of Acculturation Along the Oregon Trail," *Tebiwa* 11(2) (1968): 38-42; **Gould**, Russell T. and Mark G. Plew, "Prehistoric Salmon Fishing in the Northern Great Basin: Ecological Dynamics, Trade Offs, and Foraging Strategies," *Prehistoric Hunter-Gatherer Fishing Strategies*, Boise State University (1996); **Green**, Thomas, "Aboriginal Residential Structures in Southern Idaho," *Journal of California and Great Basin Anthropology* 15(1) (1993): 58-72; **Green**, Thomas J., Bruce Cochran, Todd Fenton, James C. Woods, Gene Titmus, Larry Tieszen, Mary Anne Davis, and Suzanne Miller, "The Buhl Burial: A Paledonian Woman from Southern Idaho," *American Antiquity* 63030 (1998): pp. 437-456; ***The Idaho Statesman***, 21 December 1992, C-1 ["It's a spiritual fiction," "Idaho really blew it"]; **Lohse**, E. S. and D. Sammons, "Southeastern Idaho Prehistory: Status and Stasis," *Idaho Archaeologist* 17(2) (1994): 35-46; **Madson**, Brigham D., *The Northern Shoshone* (Caldwell, Idaho: Caxton Printers, 1980); **Murphey**, Kelly A., "An Archaeological Survey of the Tuanna Desert Land Entries Project—South Central Idaho," *University of Idaho Anthropological Research Manuscript Series* No. 37, Moscow, Idaho (1977); **Murphey**, Kelly A., "Native American Settlement and Subsistence in Devil's Creek: Twin Falls and Owyhee Counties, Idaho," Master's Thesis, University of Idaho (1985); **Murphey**, Kelly A., "Shield-Figures, Pits and a Hole in One: The Rock Art of Upper Salmon Falls," *Idaho Archaeologist* 20(2): 23-32; **Murphey**, Kelly A. and M. J. Crutchfield, "Archaeological Test Excavations and the Crutchfield Site: Hagerman

Valley, Idaho," *University of Idaho Anthropological Reports*, No. 86, Moscow, Idaho (1985); **Murphey**, Kelly A., M. J. Freeman and Peter Bowler, "Valley of the Mighty Snake," *Hagerman Valley Historical Society Reports* No. 1, Hagerman, Idaho (1993); **Murphy**, Robert F. and Yolanda Murphy, "Shoshone/Bannock Subsistence and Society," *University of California Anthropological Records* 16(7) (1960): 293-338; **Murphy**, Robert F. and Yolanda Murphy, "Northern Shoshone and Bannock," *Handbook of North American Indians Volume II*, W. L. Azevedo, ed. (Washington D.C.: Smithsonian Institution, 1986); **Nokkentved**, N. S., "Buhl gravel pit yields prehistoric bones," *Times-News*, 20 January 1989, 1-A ["It's kind of sacred"]; **Nokkentved**, N. S., "The 10,000-year-old woman," *Times-News*, 20 December 1992, 1-A. ["This is an old burial"]; **Pavesic,** Max G. and Daniel S. Meatte, "Archaeological Test Excavations at the National Fish Hatchery Locality, Hagerman Valley, Idaho," *Boise State University Archaeological Reports*, No. 8, Boise State University (1980); **Plew**, Mark G., "Archaeological Test Excavations at Four Prehistoric Sites in the Western Snake River Canyon Near Bliss, Idaho," *Idaho Archaeological Consultants Project Reports*, No. 7, Boise, Idaho (1981); **Plew**, Mark G., "Implications of Nutritional Potential of Anadromous Fish Resources of the Western Snake River Plain," *Journal of California and Great Basin Anthropology* 5(1-2) (1983); **Silva**, Samantha, "A famous skeleton returns to the earth," *High Country News*, 8 March 1993, p. 1 ["Repatriation is a loaded and improper term," "The whole policy of dig-

A family of migrants from Texas returns to Idaho for the pea and potato harvest, 1938.

ging up graves," "the repayment of a long-standing debt"]; **Steward**, Julian H., "Basin Plateau Aboriginal Sociopolitical Groups," *Bureau of American Ethnology Bulletin*, No. 120, Washington (1938); **Woods**, James C. and Gene L. Titmus, "A Review of the Simon Clovis Collection," *Idaho Archaeologist* 8(1) (1985): 3-8.

Chapter 4: First Encounters

Ambrose, Stephen, *Undaunted Courage: Meriwether Lewis, Thomas Jefferson, and the Opening of the American West* (New York: Simon and Schuster, 1996); **Bancroft**, Hubert Howe, *History of the Northwest* (New York: Simon and Schuster, 1996) ["it was Wyeth who more directly" p. 598]; **Brandon**, William, *Mountain Men and Fur Traders of the Far West*, LeRoy R. Hafen, ed. (Lincoln: University of Nebraska Press, 1982) ["one beaver, a dog, a few wild cherries" p. 70]; **Crittenden**, Don E., *A History of the American Fur Trade of the Far West*, (Stanford: Academic Reprints, 1954); **Cross**, Osborne, *March of the Regiment of Mounted Rifleman to Oregon in Oregon in 1849* (Fairfield: Ye Galleon Press, 1967); **DeVoto**, Bernard, *Across the Wide Missouri* (Cambridge: Riverside Press, 1947) ["a stone age economy that meant"]; **DeVoto**, Bernard, *The Course of Empire* (Boston: Houghton and Mifflin, 1980); **Elliott**, T. C., ed., "The Peter Skene Ogden Journals," *The Quarterly of the Oregon Historical Society* 10(4): 331-365; **Frémont**, John C., *Report of the Exploring to the Rocky Mountains in the Year 1842 and to Oregon and North California in the Years 1843-44* (Washington: Gales and Seaton, 1845) ["strung along the river" p. 168]; **Goetzmann**, William H., *Exploration and Empire* (New York: History Book Club, 1993); **Irving**, Washington, *Astoria* (Portland: Binfords and Mort, 1950) ["Their habitations were very comfortable" pp. 258-259]; **Irving**, Washington, "The Adventures of Captain Bonneville, U.S.A.," *Rocky Mountains and the Far West*, Edgeley W. Todd, ed. (Norman: University of Oklahoma, 1961) ["to linger in" p. 256, "consisted of a mantle" pp. 221-222]; **Madsen**, Brigham D., *The Northern Shoshone* (Caldwell, Idaho: Caxton Printers, 1980); **Madsen**, Brigham D., *The Bannock of Idaho* (Moscow, Idaho: University of Idaho, 1996); **Merk**, Frederick, *History of the Westward Movement* (New York: Knopf, 1978) ["the hub of transportation" p. 264]; **Morgan**, Dale L., *Jedediah Smith and the Opening of the West* (Lincoln: University of Nebraska Press, 1953); **Murphey**, Kelly A., M. J. Freeman, and Peter Bowler, "Valley of the Mighty Snake," *Hagerman Valley Historical Society Reports*, No. 1, Hagerman, Idaho (1993); **Newman**, Peter C., *Caesars of the Wilderness: The Story of the Hudson's Bay Company* (New York: Penguin, 1987); **Preuss**, Charles, *Exploring With Frémont: The Private Diaries of Charles Preuss, Cartographer for John C. Frémont on His First, Second, and Fourth Expeditions to the Far West*, Erwin G. and Elisabeth K. Godde, transs. and eds. (Norman: University of Oklahoma Press, 1995) ["If we had only left that" p. 83, "Yesterday we passed the fishing" pp. 91-92]; **Rollins**, Phillip Ashton, ed., The *Discovery of the Oregon Trail: Robert Stuart's Narratives of His Overland Trip Eastward from Astoria in 1812-1813* (Lincoln: University of Nebraska Press, 1995) ["Whatever road one follows" p. 267, "pursue our journey by water" p. 288, "highway to the Columbia" p. 292, "his fear was so great" p. 292, "On the 28th" p. 292, "one of them led us" p. 322, "took great pains" p. 295, "the prime of fishing" p. 108, "about 100 lodges" p. 109, "considerable rapids" p. 110, "as they left the vicinity" pp. 111-113]; **Ronda**, James P., *Astoria & Empire* (Lincoln: University of Nebraska Press, 1990); **Ross**, Alexander, *Adventures of the First Settlers on the Oregon Trail or Columbia River*, reprint 1986 (Lincoln: University of Nebraska Press, 1849) ["this little bold and courageous" p. 198]; **Ross**, Alexander, *The Fur Hunters of the Far West*, Kenneth A. Spaulding, ed. (Norman: University of Oklahoma Press, 1961); **Russell**, Osborne, *Journal of a Trapper*, Aubrey L. Haines, ed. (Lincoln: University of Nebraska Press, 1965); **Steward**, Julian H., *Basin-Plateau Aboriginal Sociopolitical Groups*, Bureau of American Ethnology Bulletin 120, reprint 1970 (Salt Lake City: University of Utah Press, 1938); **Thwaites**, Reubin Gold, ed., *Travels in the Far Northwest, 1839-1846*, Vol. 24 (Chicago: The Arthur H. Clarke Company, 1905); **Utley**, Robert M., *A Life Wild and Perilous: Mountain Men and the Paths to the Pacific* (New York: Henry Holt, 1997) ["a passage by which" p. 62, "the more impoverished" p. 74]; **West**, Elliott, "American Frontier," *The Oxford History of the American West* (New York: Oxford University Press, 1994) ["a place of accommodation" pp. 139-140]; **White**, Richard, "A Precarious Balance," *The Native Americans*, Betty and Ian Ballantine, eds. (Atlanta: Turner Publishing, Inc., 1993); **Wyeth**, Nathaniel J., *Sources of the History of Oregon, Vol. 1: The Correspondence and Journals of Nathaniel J. Wyeth, 1831-1836* (Eugene, Oregon: University Press, 1899) ["from these Indians"]; **Zaslowsky**, Dyan, *These American Lands* (New York: Henry Holt and Co., 1986).

Making French fries. Southcentral Idaho annually exports more than forty-five million hundredweight of potatoes (6.2 billion burlap sacks each weighing one hundred pounds).

Chapter 5: Devil's Backbone

A.C.C., "Idaho Pioneers," (1930), Oregon Trail, vertical file, Idaho State Historical Library and Archive, Boise, Idaho; **Applegate**, Jesse A., *A Day With The Cow Column* (Fairfield, Washington: Ye Galleon Press, 1990) ["In getting away from this place" pp. 85-86, "something red in color" p. 84]; **Arrington**, Leonard J., *History of Idaho* (Moscow, Idaho: University of Idaho Press, 1994) ["excavated by the finger of God" 1:125]; **Atwood**, Rev. A., *The Conquerors: Sketches of the American Settlement of the Oregon Country* (Cincinnati: Jennings and Graham, 1907) ["Oregon would contribute" pp. 133-134]; **Beal**, Merrill D. and Merle Wells, *History of Idaho*, 3 Vols., (New York: Lewis Historical Publishing Co., 1959); **Bek**, William C., trans., "From Bethel Missouri, to Aurora, Oregon: Letters to William Keil, 1850-1870," *Missouri Historical Review* 47 (October 1953) ["Hideous world, fearful roads" pp.33-34]; **Bhatt**, Rob, "State of Conflict: the western Shoshone claim…Nevada still belongs to them," *Las Vegas Weekly*, 2 December 1999 ["How did the United States"]; **Billington**, Ray Allen, *Westward Expansion: A History of the American Frontier*, 4th ed. (New York: Macmillan Publishing Co., 1974) ["This country was once covered" p. 579]; **Bird**, Annie Laurie, *Boise: The Peace Valley* (Caldwell, Idaho: Caxton Printers, 1934) ["We bought some dried salmon" pp. 81-89]; **Brosnan**, Cornelius, J., *Jason Lee: Prophet of the New Oregon* (New York: Macmillan Company, 1932) ["impetuous fury and astonishing splendor" p. 260]; ***Capital News***, Boise, Idaho, 3 November 1930 ["The blazing for the old"]; **Coates**, F., *Hagerman: In The Valley of the Thousand Springs* (Twin Falls, Idaho: Sprint Print, 1989); **Conner** quoted in Stephen J. Crum, *The Road on Which We Came—Po'l Pentun Tammen Kimmappeh: A History of the Western Shoshone* (Salt Lake City: University of Utah, 1994) ["Leave their bodies thus exposed" p. 23]; **Cramer**, Howard A., "Thousand Springs and Salmon Falls," *Idaho Yesterdays* 18(3) (1974): 14-23 ["of small crustacea" pp. 39-40, "one horror after another" p. 20, "Wealth makes them ignorant" p. 20, "large enough to turn machinery" p. 22, "an old tin cup" p. 21]; **Cross**, Osborne, "A Report in the Form of a Journal: the March of the Regiment of Mounted Riflemen to Oregon from May 10 to October 5, 1849," Sen. Exec. Doc. 1, 31st Cong., 1st sess. (1850) ["a singular freak of nature" p. 198]; **De Voto**, Bernard, *The Year of Decision: 1846* (Boston: Little Brown, & Co., 1943) ["Year of decision … manifest destiny … a great many"]; **Dent**, Frederick T., "Report of 8 November 1860," H. Ex. Doc. 29, 36th Cong., 2nd sess. (1860) ["I often wish we had done" pp. 86-90]; **Edwin**, James, comp., *Account of an Expedition from Pittsburgh to the Rocky Mountains…under the Command of Major Stephen H. Long*, 2 Vols. (Philadelphia: H.C. Carey & I. Lea, 1823) ["In regards to this section of country" 2: 261]; **Elliott**, T. C., "The Earliest Travelers on the Oregon Trail," *Quarterly of the Oregon Historical Society* 13 (March 1912) ["The fittest to survive" p. 83]; **Fanselow**, Julie, *Traveling the Oregon Trail* (Helena, Montana: Falcon Press, 1992) ["the most tortuous road" p. 125]; **Farb**, Peter, *Man's Rise to Civilization: The Cultural Ascent of the Indians of North American*, 2nd ed. (New York: Penguin Books, 1978) ["The Shoshone had little to lose" p. 33]; **Farnham**, Thomas J., *Travels in the Great Western Prairies, the Anahuac and Rocky Mountains, and in* *the Oregon Territory* (Poughkeepsie, New York: Killey and Lossing Printers, 1841), p. 76 ["The Peorians traded," "Our ears are yet saluted," "An encampment of Bannocks"]; **Federal Writer's Project**, *The Oregon Trail*, Washington D.C. (1939) ["The biological genes" p. 33]; **Finnegan**, Lora J., "Making History Again On the Oregon Trail," *Sunset* 190 (June 1990) ["The dust was even worse" p. 82]; **Frémont**, John C., *Exploring Expedition to the Rocky Mountains, Oregon, and California*, Buffalo, New York (1849) [" A subterranean river burst" pp. 224-225]; **Ghent**, William J., *The Road To Oregon* (London: Longmans, Green and Co., 1929) ["The weather was bitterly cold" p. 221]; **Gudde**, Erwin G. and Elizabeth K. Gudde, *Exploring With Frémont: The Private Diaries of Charles Preuss, Cartographer for John C. Frémont on His First, Second, and Fourth Expeditions to the Far West* (Norman, Oklahoma: University of Oklahoma Press, 1958) ["How old man Vulcan" p. 91]; **Harthorn**, Sandy, and Kathleen Bettis, *One Hundred Years of Idaho Art, 1850-1950* (Boise, Idaho: Boise Art Museum, 1990) ["a beautiful blank" pp. 15-16]; **Henretta**, James A., et al., *America's History* (Chicago: Dorsey, 1987); **Holmes**, Kenneth L., "Francois Payette," *The Mountain Men and the Fur Trade of the Far West, 1834-1890*, 10 Vols., Leroy R. Hafen, ed. (Glendale, California: Arthur C. Clarke Co., 1965-1972) ["scarcely afforded sustenance" p. 173]; **Husbands**, Michael B., "Senator Lewis F. Linn and the Oregon Question," *Missouri Historical Review* 66 (October 1971); **Idaho State Department of Commerce and Tourism**, *Undisturbed in Idaho: Oregon Trail*, (about 1990), folder 16, box 6, Idaho Travel and Tourism Collection, MS 544, Idaho State Historical Library and Archives, Boise, Idaho ["Here we are upon a sage" p. 2]; **"Shoshone Falls,"** Reference Leaflet, Native American Tribes Population Rankings, Idaho State Historical Library and Archives ["the progress of the white settlers"]; **Irving**, quoted in Vardis Fisher, *Idaho: A Guide in Word and Picture* (Caldwell, Idaho: Caxton Printers, 1937); **Kelly**, Robert, *Looking at the Land of Promise: Pioneer Images of the Pacific Northwest* (Pullman, Washington: Washington State University Press, 1988) [Adams "To make the wilderness blossom" p. 9]; **King**, Clarence, "The Falls of the Shoshone," *Overland Monthly* (October 1870) ["a strange savage scene" p. 385]; **Laut**, Agnus C., *The Overland Trail: The Epic Path of the Pioneers to Oregon* (New York: Frederick A. Stokes Co., 1929) ["Children of Israel" pp. 3-4, 98-99]; **Longworth**, Basil, *Diary of Basil N. Longworth*, Portland, Oregon, Historical Records Survey ["fertile soil … beautiful scenery" p. 38]; **Madsen**, Bingham D., *Chief Pocatello* (Moscow, Idaho: University of Idaho Press, 1986) ["every possible means … homeless" p. 65]; **Madsen**, Bingham D., *The Northern Shoshone* (Caldwell, Idaho: Caxton Press, 1980) ["kill everything" p. 36]; **Martin**, James Kirby, et. al., *America and Its People* (Glenview, Illinois: Scott, Foresman, 1989); **Mattes**, Merrill J., "New Horizons on the Trail," *People of the Plains and the Mountains: Essays in the History of the West Dedicated to Everett Dick*, Ray Allen Billington, ed. (Westport, Connecticut: Greenwood Press, 1973); **Maury**, Reuben F., "Expedition Against the Snake Indians," *War of Rebellion, 1902*, p. 224 ["We have no fixed objective," "the principle haunt of the Snake," "expressed great desire for peace"]; **McComas**, E. S., quoted in Ingvard Henry Eide, *Oregon Trail* (Chicago: Rand McNally & Co., 1972) ["a man must be able to endure" p. 166, "burnt rocks … damned bad dust" p. 18]; **Myers**, L. Daniel, "A Review of the Historical Literature from the Bliss Dam to the Salmon Dam Area, Snake River Plain Region, Southern Idaho," A report to the Shoshone-Paiute Tribes, Fort Hall Reservation (1992) ["When the Snake River was reached" p. 74, "those Indians who are more hostile" p. 50]; **Nye**, Russel B., "Parkman, Red Fated, and White Civilization," *Essays on American Literature on Honor of Jay B. Hubbel*, Clarence Gohdes, ed., (Durham, North Carolina: Duke University, 1967) ["Were not in the slightest" pp. 152-163]; **Oregon-California Trail Association,** "Preservation Activities," http://trib.com/~lwisch/preserve.html (cited April 25, 2000); **Parkman**, Francis, *The Oregon Trail* (New York: Penguin Books, 1982) ["The Indians will soon be abased" pp. 17, 20]; **"Pioneers, O Pioneers,"** Old Oregon Trail Centennial Celebration Souvenir Program, Oregon Trail, vertical files, Idaho State Historical Library and Archives ["and exact historical reproduction"]; **Shannon**, Donald H., *The Utter Disaster on the Oregon Trail* (Caldwell, Idaho: Snake Country Publishing, 1993) ["Snake country massacres" and "non-mythical trail tragedies" pp. xvi-xvii, "real massacres" p. 97, "came to our wagon" p. 29]; **Turner**, Frederick Jackson, *The Turner Thesis: Concerning the Role of the Frontier in American History*, George Rogers Taylor, ed. (Lexington, Massachusetts: D.C. Health & Co., 1972) ["The frontier was the most" pp. 5, 27, "Stand at the Cumberland Gap" p. 10]; **U.S. Bureau of Land Management**, *Emigrant Trails of Southern Idaho* (Boise, Idaho: U.S. Bureau of Land Management State Office, 1989) ["wrecked and ruined" p. 68]; **U.S. Department of the Interior,** National Park Service, *Comprehensive Management Use Plan Update, Final Environmental Impact Statement, Oregon National Historic Trail*, compact disc publication (October 1999) ["A symbol of westward expansion" pp.4, 25, 35, 209-216]; **Webber**, Bert, ed., *Oregon Trail Diaries of Twin Sisters Cecilia Adams and Parthenia Blank in 1852* (Medford, Oregon: Webb Research Group, 1992), p. 59 ["Dull sale," "mill sites enough for the whole state"]; **Whitman**, Narcissa, "Diary" in Clifford Drury, *First White Woman over the Rockies: Diaries, Letters, and Biographical Sketches*, 3 Vols. (Glendale, California: Arthur H. Clark Co., 1963) p. 120 ["We were met," "It was a great wonder"].

Chapter 6: Staking Claim

Beal, Merrill D., *A History of Southeastern Idaho* (Caldwell, Idaho: Caxton Printers, 1942) ["red barbarity" p. 238]; **Bever**, Betty B., *Idaho and the Magic Circle: How They Came to Be* (Caldwell, Idaho: Caxton Printers, 2000) ["bright and warm" p. 7, "the dam is deep" p. 239]; **Beiter**, Pat, "Reluctant Shepherds: The Basques in Idaho," *Basques of the Pacific Northwest*, Richard Etulain, ed. (Pocatello, Idaho: Idaho State University Press, 1991); **Chen**, Yong, "The Internal Origins of Chinese Emigration to California Reconsidered," *Western Historical Quarterly* 28(4): 520-546; **Coates**, Gaye, *Hagerman: In The Valley of the Thousand Springs*, Twin Falls, Idaho (1989); **Conley**, Cort, *Idaho for the Curious* (Cambridge, Idaho: Backeddy Books, 1982) ["Ten to fifteen arrests per day" p. 532]; **Cook**, Dick, Personal communication, 24 October 1995; **Cook**, Dick and Vay Cook, Oral history, National Park Service, Hagerman, Idaho (1997, 1998); **Daily Utah Reporter**, Corinne, Utah (1870); **Egleston**, Thomas, "The Treatment of Fine Gold in the Sands of Snake River, Idaho," *Transactions of the American Institute of Mining Engineers*: (18): 597-609 [The heavier pieces of the black sand" p. 598]; **Fiege**, Mark, *Irrigated Eden: The Making of an Agricultural Landscape in the American West* (Seattle: University of Washington Press, 1999) ["God a sort of chief engineer" p. 23, "clubbed the desert" p. 174, "there will be better transportation" p. 177, "realize progress" p. 180]; **Gridley**, Asahel, Oral history, National Park

Service, Hagerman, Idaho (1997, 1998); **Hagerman Mining Book**, Original records of the Salmon Falls Mining District, 1878-1884, Unpublished, copy on file at the Hagerman Historical Society Museum, Hagerman, Idaho; **Hawley**, James H., *History of Idaho*, Vol. 1 (Chicago: S. J. Clarke Publishing Co., 1920); **Hopkins**, Earl, Twin Falls Public Library Oral History Project: Tape 6; *The Idaho Statesman* 23 March 1870 ["as high as \$40"]; *The Idaho Statesman* 19 May 1870 ["a very fine yacht," "splendor

almost indescribable"]; *The Idaho Statesman* 30 July 1870 ["so fine and light," "For rattlesnakes, scorpions, mosquitoes, gnats, sage-brush," "where the water is very swift"]; *The Idaho Statesman* 21 January 1871 ["The Chinese are better adept"]; *The Idaho Statesman* May 1879 ["claims adjoining his"]; *Idaho Tri-Weekly Statesman*, 7 June 1881 ["horse restaurant"]; **James**, Ronald L., *Ruins of a World: Chinese Gold Mining at the Mon-Tung Site in the Snake River Canyon*, U.S. Department of the Interior, Bureau of Land Management, Idaho Cultural Resource Series No. 4; **James**, Ronald L., Lorainne Gross, and Teri DeYoung, "Hagerman Area Mining History," Report on file with Idaho Power Company, Environmental Affairs Department, Boise, Idaho (1995) ["metropolis of the river"]; **Kuhn**, J. S., *Irrigation: Being a Brief Treatise Compiled from Authoritative Sources* (Pittsburgh: Municipal & Corporation Securities Co., 1908) ["Rainfall farming" p. 7]; **Madsen**, Brigham D., "The Almo 'Massacre' Revisited," *Idaho Yesterdays* 37 (Fall 1993): 54-64; **Mercer**, Laurie and Carole Simon-Smolinski, eds., *Idaho's Ethnic Heritage*, 3 Vols. (Boise, Idaho: Idaho Centennial Commission, 1990) ["an absolute genius" 1:65, "just walked out" 2:14]; **Murphy**, John Mortimer, *Rambles in North-western America: From the Pacific Ocean to the Rocky Mountains* (London: Chapman Hall, 1879) ["a hamlet composed of a few" pp. 180-181]; **Murphey**, Kelly, M. J. Freeman, and Peter Bowler, *Valley of the Mighty Snake: An Overview of the Cultural and Natural History of Hagerman Valley*, Hagerman Valley Historical Society Report, No. 1 (1993); **Newcomb**, Robinson, Charles W. Merrill, and R. L. Kiessling, *Employment and Income From Gold Placering By Hand Methods, 1935-37*, Works Project Administration, National Research Project, in cooperation with the Department of the Interior, Bureau of Mines, Report No. E-14, Philadelphia, Pennsylvania (1940); **New York Times**, 23 June 1878 ["Starvation is staring them"]; **Owyhee Avalanche**, Silver City, Idaho (1870) ["Bob Drummond got back"]; **Quinn**, Larry, *A History of the Magic Valley* (Twin Falls, Idaho: Publishing West Associates, 1996) ["The attackers took scalps" pp. 76-77]; **Quinton**, Karen, ed., *Life in the Saddle of the South Idaho Desert: The Stories of Thomas Ike Gray*, Twin Falls, Idaho (1988) ["the engine came around" p. 131]; **Roberts**, Edward, *Shoshone and Other Western Wonders* (New York: Harper and Brothers, 1888); **Rohe**, Randall, "Chinese River Mining in the West," *Montana: The Magazine of Western History* 46(3) (1996): 14-29 [Invariably the Chinese" and "many a claim, abandoned in despair" p. 19]; **Ross**, Arnold, *Indian Wars of Idaho* (Caldwell, Idaho: Caxton Press, 1932) ["such an act of treachery" pp. 209-210]; **Ross** D. W., "Biennial Report of the State Engineer to the Governor of Idaho for the Years of 1899-1900," (Boise, Idaho: Capitol Printing Office) ["Laugh at the cloudless skies" p. 7]; **Ryan**, John F., *History of Camas County*, Fairfield, Idaho (1975), p. 4 ["there is a fine market," "soldiers of peace"]; **Scholl**, B. Frank, ed., *Library of Health: Complete Guide to Preventions and Cure of Disease* (Philadelphia: Historical Publishing Company, 1925) ["to relieve pain and irritation" p. 1420]; **Schwantes**, Carlos, *In Mountain Shadows: A History of Idaho* (Lincoln, Nebraska: University of Nebraska Press, 1991) ["Put money into commercial ventures" p. 91]; **See Idaho First**, "The Ancient City of Springtown," 19 September 1914: pp. 22-23; **Spence**, Clark C., *For Wood River or Bust: Idaho's Silver Boom of the 1880s* (Moscow, Idaho: University of Idaho Press, 1999) ["Hailey-born Ezra Pound disparaged"]; **Stricker**, Lucy, "Area Pioneer to Get Honor Today," From an interview with Mrs. Lucy Stricker printed week of 9 May 1942 in an unidentified Magic Valley publication provided by Bev Stone; **Twin Falls News**, 10 July 1914 ["invading the city"]; **Twin Falls: The "Magic City,"** (1910), Twin Falls, Idaho, MS 544, Box 8, pam 22, Idaho State Historical Library and Archives ["Undoubtedly the most metropolitan," "a system of drainage"]; **Quinn**, Larry, *A History of the Magic Valley* (Twin Falls, Idaho: Publishing West Associates, 1996) ["The attackers took scalps" pp. 76-77]; **Walgamott**, Charles S., *Reminiscences of Early Days*, Twin Falls, Idaho (1926) ["was asked to ferry over several Chinamen" p. 62]; **Walgamott**, Charles S., *Six Decades Back* (Caldwell, Idaho: Caxton Printers, 1936) ["the bodies of the unfortunate" p. 126]; **Wells**, Merle, *Gold Campus and Silver Cities* (Moscow, Idaho: Department of Land and Bureau of Mines and Geology, 1983); **White**, Richard, *It's Your Misfortune and None of My Own: A History of the American West* (Norman: University of Oklahoma Press, 1991) ["a blood bond" p. 618]; **Worth**, Clark D., "Idaho Made the Desert Bloom" *National Geographic Magazine* 85 (June 1944): pp. 641-686 ["Truly magic it is" p. 653, "in each irrigation born town" p. 683]; **Wright**, Patricia, *Twin Falls Country: A Look at Idaho Architecture* (Boise, Idaho: Idaho State Historical Society Preservation Office, 1979) ["Just to think" p. 8].

Chapter 7: Skull in the Quarry

Akersten, William A. and Mary E. Thompson, *The Hagerman Horse Quarry: History, Status, Potential, and Recommendations for the Future*, National Park Service (1992) ["to preserve for the benefit"]; **Boss**, Norman, Hagerman, to Alexander Wetmore, Washington, 25 September 1931, Smithsonian Archives, Record Unit 305, Box 577, Accession No. 109128; **Bowler**, Aldrich, Oral history, Hagerman Fossil Beds National Monument (1996) ["They had a bad map," "it takes a long time"]; *Capital News*, Boise, Idaho, 5 August 1931 ["the liquid would boil eggs"]; *Capital News*, Boise, Idaho, 26 September 1935 ["force the large institutions"]; **Carr**, Ethan, *Wilderness by Design: Landscape, Architecture, & the National Park Service* (Lincoln: University of Nebraska Press, 1998); **Cook**, Dick and Vay Cook, Oral history, Mathew Henbest and Bob Willhite, Hagerman, Idaho, 24 June 1996 ["what in the hell," "an old man with a white," "tall and dark," "The worst thing he ever"]; **Erwin**, Mrs. Richard P., Boise, to James Gidley, Washington, 26 April 1931, Smithsonian Archives, Record Unit 305, Box 577, Accession No. 109128 ["third and final trip"]; **Gazin**, C. Lewis, "Fossil Hunting in

Graffiti, I-84 at Malad Gorge. Left: downtown Twin Falls, 1941.

Southern Idaho," *Field Work of the Smithsonian Institution*, 12 September 1934 ["We retrieved most," "The exposed surface," "an adult and two young"]; **Gidley**, James, "Hunting Fossils on the Old Oregon Trail," *Smithsonian Explorations* (1929) ["If we had discovered" p. 29, "To the fossil hunter" p. 33]; **Gidley**, James W., American Falls, to Alexander Wetmore, Washington, 21 July 1929, Smithsonian Archives, Record Unit 305, Box 577, Accession No. 109128 ["I agree with you"]; **Gidley**, James W., Hagerman, to Charles Gilmore, Washington, 13 August 1929, Smithsonian Archives, Record Unit 305, Box 577, Accession No. 109128 ["They are in soft sand"]; **Gidley**, James W., Washington, to Mrs. Richard P. Erwin, Boise, 15 May 1931, Smithsonian Archives, Record Unit 305, Box 577, Accession No. 109128 ["The natural result"]; **Gridley**, Asahel, Oral history, Bob Willhite, Hagerman, Idaho (1997); **Hibbard**, Claude, "A New Weasel from the Lower Pleistocene of Idaho," *Journal of Mammalogy* (May 1958): 245-246; *Idaho Evening Statesman*, Steve Ahrens column, 14 June 1968 ["I'm no promoter,"]; *The Idaho Statesman*, "Farmers oppose fossil area," 14 December 1976: p. 3 ["nobody seems to want," "development of thousands of acres," "equipping a national monument,"]; *The Idaho Statesman*, Jim MacLean column, 27 May 1954 ["systematically looted"]; *The Idaho Statesman*, Editorial, 22 December 1976 ["historical treasure," "hundreds of thousand acres"]; **Jefferson**, Thomas, "Notes on the State of Virginia," New York (1664) ["this reproach is as unjust" p. 69]; **King**, Neil, "Back to Our Future," *Equus Evolves* (Boise, Idaho: Black Canyon Communications, 2002) ["Cultural and natural resources"]; **Macdonald**, James Reid, "Dig that Horse Heaven," *Quarterly*, Los Angeles County Museum of Natural History, No. 2 (Fall 1966): 12-14; **McDonald**, H. Gregory, "More Than Just Horses," *Rocks and Minerals*, (September/October 1993): 322-326; **Muir**, John, *The Yosemite* (1912) ["Everybody needs beauty" p. 256]; **Nash**, Roderick, *Wilderness and the American Mind* (New Haven: Yale University Press, 1967), 67-122 ["One must be astonished"]; **Rothman**, Hal, *America's National Monuments: The Politics of Preservation* (Urbana: University of Illinois Press, 1989); **Runte**, Alfred, *National Parks: The American Experience* (Lincoln: University of Nebraska Press, 1989), pp. 11-12 ["When national parks," "to preserve the spectacular sites," "pragmatic alliance"]; **Wetmore**, Alexander, Washington, to W. D. Matthews, Berkley, 15 March 1930, Smithsonian Archives, Record Unit 305, Box 577, Accession No. 109128 ["We expect to develop this site,"]; **Wheeler** C. S., Letter, Paleontology #1, vertical files, Idaho State Historical Library and Archives (1933) ["very wonderful in appearance"]; **Worster**, Donald, *Nature's Economy: A History of Ecological Ideas* (Cambridge: University Press, 1977) ["Why should man" p. 185, "A well-handled farm" p. 267].

Chapter 8: Route 30

Balch, Glenn, "Southern Idaho boasts real city of 'magic,'" *Twin Falls Daily Times*, 6 September 1928; **Barber**, Floyd and Dan Martin, *Idaho in the Pacific Northwest* (Caldwell: Caxton Printers, 1956), pp. 220-223; **Belasco**, Warren James, *Americans on the Road: From Autocamp to Motel, 1910-1945* (Cambridge: The Massachusetts Institute of Technology Press, 1979) ["uncomfortable necessities which must be employed" and "huge, clumsy affairs" p. 20, "We are seeing the country" p. 29]; **Buckendorf**, Glenn, Interview by Todd Shallat, 5 January 2002 ["That was before the corners were banked"]; **Francaviglia**,

Richard V., *The Mormon Landscape: Existence, Creation, and Perception of a Unique Image in the American West* (New York: Arno Press, 1978), p. 47; **Jennings**, Jan, ed., *Roadside America: The Automobile in Design and Culture* (Ames, Iowa: University Press for the Society for Commercial Archaeology, 1990); **Johnson**, David, "Growing farm area a basis for advance," *Idaho Daily Statesman* (1947), vertical files, Idaho State Historical Library and Archives ["What is needed is 50,000 more votes"]; **Kuralt**, Charles, "U.S. Highways: From US 1 to US 830," www.us-highways.com (cited June 28, 2002), ["thanks to the interstate highway system"]; **Magic Valley Yesterdays Committee**, *Magic Valley Yesterdays: Your Souvenir Book*, Twin Falls (1947), vertical files, Idaho State Historical Library and Archives; **Rose**, Mark H., *Interstate Express Highway Politics 1941-1989* (Knoxville: University of Tennessee, 1990), pp. 114-117; **Schifferdecker**, Jerry, "Idaho auto death per mileage rate ranks among nation's highest," *Idaho Daily Statesman*, 22 December 1972; **Twin Falls Chamber of Commerce**, "Your Place in the Sun," Twin Falls (1961), vertical files, Idaho State Historical Library, ["Idaho's bright spot"]; **Weingroff**, Richard F., "The Federal Highway Act of 1956: Creating the Interstate System," *Public Roads* (Summer 1996) ["magic motorways" p. 96].

Chapter 9: Making Magic

Barbour, Michael G., "Ecological Fragmentation in the Fifties," *Uncommon Ground: Toward Reinventing Nature*, William Cronon, ed. (New York: W. W. Norton, 1995) ["more complex than we can think" p. 247]; **Chapman**, Sherl L., "Irrigated Agriculture: Idaho's Economic Lifeblood," Idaho Water Users Association, http://www.iwua.org/history/idhistory.html (cited July 17, 2001) ["The development of Idaho's irrigation capacity"]; **Donworth**, Dan, "Dam Facts about a Dead Dam," *Idaho Mountain Express*, http://www.mtexpress.com/1998/07-01-98/snakedam.html (cited July 17, 2001 ["Blow the dams"]; **Hoyt**, Jyl, "The Snake: Idaho's Working River," Idaho Public Radio, November 11, 1993 ["It makes me feel good"]; **Idaho Department of Health and Welfare**, Idaho Water Quality Status Report, Boise, Idaho (1998) ["a water-quality-limited-segment" p. 44]; **Idaho Nature Conservancy Field Notes**, "A Balancing Act: Giving New Life to the Middle Snake River" (Spring/ Summer 2000) ["The most polluted"]; **Perry**, Thomas Sargeant, "Mountains in Literature," *Atlantic Monthly* 44 (September 1879) ["We have grown accustomed" p. 302]; **Reisner**, Mark, *Cadillac Desert* (New York: Viking Press, 1994) ["We set out to tame the rivers" p. 505].

Photo Credits

Museum of American History, Smithsonian Institution; p. 98 adapted from Herman J. Viola "Wilkes and Frémont Expeditions" *Exploring the West* (1987); p. 99 John Charles Frémont *Memoirs of My Life* (1886); p. 100 (top) #1706 Smithsonian, (bottom) courtesy Idaho State Historical Museum; pp. 100-101 Bill West courtesy The Herrett Center for Arts and Science, College of Southern Idaho.

The Devil's Backbone: pp. 102-104 James Frost; p. 105 W. H. D. Koerner, Buffalo Bill Historical Center; p. 107 #LC-USZC4-3252-D Library of Congress; pp. 108-109 James Frost; pp. 110-112 #X-11929 Denver Public Library; pp. 110-113 James Frost; pp. 114-115 #X-32265 Denver Public Library; p. 116 (top) #H-419 Denver Public Library, (middle) #X-32309 Denver Public Library, (bottom) #X-32266 Denver Public Library; p. 117 #X-32250 Denver Public Library; p. 122 #X-32285 Denver Public Library; p. 123 courtesy Bill Chachula; p. 124-125 courtesy Idaho State Historical Museum; p. 122 (bottom) J. Capps & Sons, LTD Catalogue (1913); p. 125 Paramount Pictures; p. 128 courtesy Twin Falls Public Library; p. 129 James Frost; pp. 130-131 #0127.1090 Frank Tenney Johnson, Gilcrease Museum.

Staking Claim: pp. 132-133 #RG 2608-1943 Simon D. Butcher Collection, Nebraska State Historical Society; p. 134 courtesy Idaho State Historical Museum; p. 135 # 73-66.1 Idaho State Historical Society; pp. 136-137 #77-69.3 Idaho State Historical Society; p. 133 James Frost; p. 134 (top) James Frost; pp. 134-135 courtesy Twin Falls Public Library; p. 137 (top) James Frost; p. 138 James Frost; p. 140 #65-166.33 Idaho State Historical Society; p. 140 #61-6-27 Idaho State Historical Society; pp. 140-141 #LC-USZ62-52430-D Library of Congress; p. 142 #75-209.2 Idaho State Historical Society; p. 143 courtesy Gem County Historical Society; p. 144 #1268-A Idaho State Historical Society; p. 145 (top) courtesy Idaho State Historical Museum, (bottom & inset) courtesy Ronald L. James; p. 146 #1316 Bob Limbert courtesy Boise State University Library Special Collections; p. 147 #77-1552 Idaho State Historical Society, (inset) courtesy Idaho State Historical Museum; p. 148 #37-B Idaho State Historical Society; pp. 148-149 James Frost; p. 150 #X-21519 Denver Public Library, (inset) James Frost; p. 149 James Frost, (inset) courtesy Ralph Peters; p. 150 #73-221.193 Idaho State Historical Society; p. 153 courtesy Robert McCarl; p. 154 #1868-H Idaho State Historical Society; p. 155 James Frost; pp. 156-157 #72-139.1 Idaho State Historical Society; p. 155 (top) James Frost, (bottom) Oregon State Historical Society; p. 156 Steve Bly; p. 157 #73-221.787 Idaho State Historical Society; p. 160 James Frost; p. 161 #77-2.33 Idaho State Historical Society; pp. 162-163 #73-221.641/d Idaho State Historical Society; p. 163 (top) courtesy Twin Falls Public Library, (bottom) MS 544 Idaho State Historical Society; pp. 164-165 James Frost; p. 165 Pacific Railroad Survey; p. 166 James Frost; p167 #83-17961 Idaho State Historical Society; pp. 168-169 James Frost; pp. 170-171 #HAER,ID,27-TWIF,1-174 Library of Congress; p. 172-173 courtesy Twin Falls Public Library; p. 174 MS 544 Idaho State Historical Society; p. 175 Kirk Anderson; pp. 176-177 #HAER,ID,42-TWIFA,1-8 Library of Congress; p. 178 (inset) courtesy Jerome County Idaho Farm Museum; pp. 180-181 James Frost.

Angler's Lounge, Hagerman.

Skull in the Quarry: pp. 182-183 courtesy Hagerman Fossil Beds National Monument; pp. 184-185 Arthur Lake, Peabody Museum of Natural History, Yale University, New Haven, CT; p. 183 #77-10004 Smithsonian Institution; p. 184 #LC-USZ262-52000-D Library of Congress; p. 185 courtesy Neil King; pp. 188-191 Archie B. Teater courtesy Idaho Community Foundation; p. 189 #312408 American Museum of Natural History Library; p. 190-192 courtesy Hagerman Fossil Beds National Monument; p. 191 courtesy Idaho State Historical Museum, (inset) courtesy Dick Cook, (bottom) #80-86.2 Idaho State Historical Society; p. 193 #80-86.16 Idaho State Historical Society; pp. 194-196 James Frost; p. 196 #80-86.3 Idaho State Historical Society; pp. 196-197 James Frost; p. 198 (top) National Postal Museum, Smithsonian Institution, (bottom) Hagerman Fossil Beds National Monument; p. 199 #19488 American Museum of Natural History Library; pp. 200-202 James Frost; p. 204 (inset) Smithsonian Institution; pp. 202-203 James Frost.

Route 30: pp. 204-215 James Frost; p. 211 courtesy Twin Falls Public Library.

Making Magic: pp. 216-217 Darin Oswald courtesy *The Idaho Statesman*; pp. 218-219 courtesy Twin Falls Public Library; p. 220 (inset) courtesy Jerome County Idaho Farm Museum; p. 220-221 David R. Frazier; p. 220-221 #HAER,ID,27-TWIF.V,1-87 Library of Congress; p. 223 #HAER,ID,42-TWIFA, 1-20 Library of Congress; p. 224 #HAER,ID,42-TWIFA,1-10 Library of Congress; pp. 224-225 Glenn Oakley; pp. 226-227 David R. Frazier; pp. 228-229 Darin Oswald courtesy *The Idaho Statesman*.

Back Matter: p. 231 #LC-USF34-018187-E Library of Congress.; p. 232 David R. Frazier; p. 234 #LC-USF34-039006-D Library of Congress; p. 237 James Frost.

Index